Drawings from New York Collections   II

Drawings from New York Collections
II
THE SEVENTEENTH CENTURY IN ITALY

Felice Stampfle, Jacob Bean

The Metropolitan Museum of Art
The Pierpont Morgan Library

Distributed by New York Graphic Society, Greenwich, Connecticut

Exhibited at The Pierpont Morgan Library, February 23–April 22, 1967

c C

Foreword

THIS EXHIBITION is the second in a comprehensive series inaugurated in November 1965, which illustrates the art of drawing through the resources of public and private collections located in New York City and its suburbs. Organized jointly by The Pierpont Morgan Library and The Metropolitan Museum of Art, the exhibitions alternate between the two institutions, the first, of the Italian Renaissance, having been shown at the Metropolitan, the second now taking place at the Morgan Library. Each exhibition is commemorated in a catalogue, in which every drawing is fully described and illustrated.

This series was a cooperative venture in which the Metropolitan's late Director, James J. Rorimer, took particular pleasure, participating actively in its planning, reading with a close critical eye the printer's proof of the first catalogue, and presiding at the inaugural exhibition. We shall carry on the projected series, but with a deep sense of loss.

Italian painting of the seventeenth century aroused little enthusiasm among Americans in the first half of the twentieth century. It is all the more gratifying that we have been able to assemble so representative a selection of drawings of the period from within our immediate area. To be sure, we have been fortunate as before in being able to borrow from collectors who began their buying as Europeans, but it is also evident that recently in this country museums and their patrons increasingly appreciate seventeenth-century Italian drawings and paintings.

Many of the same private collectors who contributed to the first exhibition have also come forward generously with loans to the second; to them and to the other lenders we express our deep gratitude. Once again we have been able to rely on the discrimination and scholarship of the curators of the drawings collections of the two sponsoring institutions, Felice Stampfle at the Morgan Library and Jacob Bean at the Metropolitan Museum. They have shared the considerable tasks of selecting the exhibition and writing the catalogue.

FREDERICK B. ADAMS, JR.
The Pierpont Morgan Library

ARTHUR A. HOUGHTON, JR.
The Metropolitan Museum of Art

Introduction

FIRST and foremost a selection of fine drawings, this exhibition offers as well a succinct illustrated history of major and minor currents in Italian art of the seventeenth century. As in the past, draughtsmanship through that century was the fundamental artistic discipline and the understructure of the finished artistic product. For the Italian artist, *disegno* was more than simple draughtsmanship—the word also embraced the intellectual concept or design that is the essential form of the work of art.

The chronological turn from the sixteenth to the seventeenth century does **not** present a clear-cut stylistic watershed. The ornamental elaboration of late mannerist draughtsmanship persisted well into the new century, with *retardataire* figures such as Camillo Procaccini and Cristofano Roncalli, while already in the last years of the sixteenth century there appeared in the drawings of Annibale Carracci a broad, freer handling, a new, more immediate approach to nature that announced the full seventeenth century.

Rome in the seventeenth century was the unquestioned artistic capital of Italy and of Europe. All the major artists in the exhibition—Annibale Carracci, Reni, Domenichino, Guercino, Cortona, Bernini, Castiglione, Rosa, Maratti—worked extensively in Rome, drawn there by the promise of lucrative commissions involved in vast programs of building and decoration. Many of the most important Roman decorative enterprises of the century are documented in this show—from the Galleria of the Palazzo Farnese (Annibale Carracci) through the Palazzo Barberini (Cortona, Sacchi) to the Palazzo Altieri (Canuti, Maratti). The continuing embellishment of St. Peter's is recorded in designs by Cortona and Maratti for the mosaics in the side aisles of Carlo Maderno's nave.

In the highly sophisticated Roman milieu, new subjects, many of them Bolognese in invention, came into vogue. It was in Rome that landscape gained its independence. The pioneering example of the Carracci in Bologna inspired Domenichino, then Mola and Grimaldi; and by the end of the century the new subject was being put to purely decorative use by artists like Crescenzio Onofri. Portraiture flourished in all media. A minor but typical figure, Ottavio Leoni, made a specialty of portrait drawings. The great sculptor Bernini drew heads of striking psychological penetration, recording in one instance the features of Cardinal Scipione Borghese, a princely patron of the period. Alongside, or rather behind, official portraiture, there grew up a new style of immediate, satiric notation, which came to be called caricature. This new form, originating in the innovating studio of the Carracci, was developed by Guercino, Mola, and Bernini. Parallel to caricature ran the *scherzi di fantasia*, those mysterious, fantastic inventions that reveal the high level of artistic intelligence and imagination in the period. Castiglione, Testa, and Rosa were gifted specialists in this new art.

Though Roman fashion reigned unchallenged, there was lively artistic activity in lesser Italian centers. To Florence, which had become somewhat provincial, Cortona brought the Roman grand style, in his decorations of the Palazzo Pitti. His frescoes in the Camera della Stufa and the state rooms of the Pitti are well documented here, and the extent of his influence is apparent in the drawings of Volterrano and Gabbiani. A conservative local tradition persisted, however. Empoli and Cigoli, who straddle the sixteenth and seventeenth centuries, are highly competent artists and as figure draughtsmen worthy descendants of Andrea del Sarto. Giovanni da San Giovanni, Cecco Bravo, and Stefano della Bella are witty and highly personal Tuscans.

In Bologna the robust academic tradition originating in the Carracci studio was enriched by the pictorial experiments of Guido Reni and Guercino. This strong local school produced artistic personalities as varied as Cantarini, Canuti, G. M. Mitelli, and Burrini.

A persistent Flemish influence is evident in Genoa's taste for animal painting and pastoral scenes, demonstrated in drawings by G. B. Castiglione and his son Francesco. Gregorio de' Ferrari and the two Piolas catered, on the other hand, to the Genoese partiality for lighthearted ornamentation.

The seventeenth was the great century for the Neapolitan school. The Bolognese Domenichino and the Parmese Lanfranco were both active and influential in Naples. Earlier in the century the powerful realistic style of Caravaggio (who is unknown as a draughtsman) exerted a formidable influence on the local school. From these crosscurrents emerged a number of strongly personal artists—Caracciolo, Falcone, Preti, Rosa, Cavallino—all present in the exhibition.

Milan and all of Lombardy were somewhat slow in accepting new styles and continued far into the century to follow late mannerist examples for the narrative cycles so popular in this region (Tanzio da Varallo, Discepoli). Venice, becalmed in the past in spite of the presence of the spirited Genoese Strozzi, maintained a tradition of grand-scale civic painting exemplified by Celesti's design for a painting once in a municipal building at Brescia.

There are marked stylistic and technical differences between Renaissance drawings and those of the seventeenth century: an increased freedom in handling, a more rapid line, a broader use of wash for more dramatic, painterly effects of light and shade, a more general use of softer chalks. Old, precise techniques, such as metalpoint on prepared paper, disappear. The often inspired use of freer techniques in the service of new pictorial researches resulted in drawings that take their place among the finest in the European tradition. The chalk drawings of Annibale Carracci, Cortona, and Bernini, the pen and wash drawings of Guercino and Rosa, the oil sketches of Castiglione (all amply and in some cases richly represented in the exhibition), are high points in the history of Italian draughtsmanship.

If in recent years there has been a widespread revival of interest in Italian art, the marks of distinguished collectors of the eighteenth and nineteenth centuries on many drawings attest the uninterrupted appreciation of the period. The collections of the Richardsons, father and son, Mariette, Vivant Denon, Sir Thomas Lawrence, the Earls of Warwick, and many other discriminating *amateurs* are represented here.

The history of drawing collecting in New York was discussed in the preface to the first catalogue of this series, but mention should again be made of the importance of Pierpont Morgan's acquisition in 1910 of the Fairfax Murray collection, the source of a number of the outstanding sheets in the exhibition. Homage should be paid, as well, to the pioneering of Janos Scholz, who for thirty years has been acquiring seventeenth-century drawings and has brought together an exceptionally representative collection. Two younger collectors, Robert and Bertina Suida Manning, have been most active in this field, forming an impressive collection of paintings and drawings. The important seventeenth-century drawings at the Metropolitan Museum have, on the whole, been acquired in fairly recent years, as have many of the drawings lent by private owners. The same is true of a number of significant sheets in the Morgan Library.

The present selection drawn from the resources of New York has been made in an attempt to give as balanced a picture as possible of draughtsmanship in seventeenth-century Italy. These resources are today considerable and have enabled us to present a selection that is more truly representative of a period than was the previous exhibition. Indeed, New York holdings are already so varied and substantial that a number of interesting drawings have regretfully had to be excluded, not only because of limitations of space but to achieve a mixture of the right proportions. Our particular intention has been to emphasize the major innovators of the century.

Once again the catalogue entries are arranged chronologically, the date of an artist's birth determining his place in the sequence, without regard to local schools. The bibliography is selective, limited to essential references. A list of works and exhibitions cited in abbreviated form precedes the catalogue notices. Only those exhibitions recorded in a descriptive catalogue are listed.

We are deeply indebted to the collectors and institutions that have lent so freely to this second exhibition. Walter Vitzthum, Denis Mahon, Philip Pouncey, and Michael Mahoney have very kindly supplied advice on specific points. Elaine Evans Dee, Assistant Curator at the Morgan Library, and Linda Boyer, Curatorial Assistant at the Metropolitan Museum, have been involved in every stage of the preparation of this catalogue. We are grateful to them for their expert professional assistance, as we are to Ruth Kraemer and Pamela Osborn McVeigh for their helpfulness in a variety of tasks. Merritt Safford and Alexander J. Yow, Conservators at the Metropolitan Museum and the Morgan Library respectively, have given useful technical advice.

FELICE STAMPFLE
Curator of Drawings and Prints
The Pierpont Morgan Library

JACOB BEAN
Curator of Drawings
The Metropolitan Museum of Art

Lenders to the Exhibition

Mr. and Mrs. Lester F. Avnet

Curtis O. Baer

Walter C. Baker

The Cooper Union Museum

J. Theodor Cremer

Donald P. Gurney

Mrs. Richard Krautheimer

Robert and Bertina Suida Manning

Janos Scholz

Benjamin Sonnenberg

Anonymous lender

Table of Contents

Works Cited in an Abbreviated Form

Baldinucci, *Notizie*
Filippo Baldinucci, *Notizie de' professori del disegno da Cimabue in qua*, 21 vols., Florence, 1767-1774.

Bartsch
Adam Bartsch, *Le Peintre graveur*, 21 vols., Vienna, 1803-1821.

Bean, *100 European Drawings*
Jacob Bean, *100 European Drawings in The Metropolitan Museum of Art*, New York, 1964.

Bellori, Piacentini edition
Giovan Pietro Bellori, *Vite di Guido Reni, Andrea Sacchi e Carlo Maratti, trascritte dipl. dal manoscritto M.S. 2506 della Biblioteca Municipale di Rouen*, Michelangelo Piacentini, ed., Rome, 1942.

Blunt, *Castiglione and Della Bella at Windsor*
Anthony Blunt, *The Drawings of G. B. Castiglione and Stefano della Bella . . . at Windsor Castle*, London, 1954.

Blunt and Cooke, *Roman Drawings at Windsor*
Anthony Blunt and Hereward Lester Cooke, *The Roman Drawings of the XVII and XVIII Centuries . . . at Windsor Castle*, London, 1960.

Brauer and Wittkower
Heinrich Brauer and Rudolf Wittkower, *Die Zeichnungen des Gianlorenzo Bernini*, 2 vols., Berlin, 1931.

Briganti, *Cortona*
Giuliano Briganti, *Pietro da Cortona, o della pittura barocca*, Florence, 1962.

Briquet
C. M. Briquet, *Les Filigranes. Dictionnaire historique des marques du papier*, 4 vols., Geneva, 1907.

Calvi, *Notizie*
Jacopo Alessandro Calvi, *Notizie della vita, e delle opere del Cavaliere Gioan Francesco Barbieri detto il Guercino da Cento*, Bologna, 1808.

Campbell, *Cortona*
Florence, Gabinetto Disegni e Stampe degli Uffizi, "Mostra di disegni di Pietro Berrettini da Cortona per gli affreschi di Palazzo Pitti," 1965 (exhibition catalogue by Malcolm Campbell).

Fairfax Murray
C. Fairfax Murray, *Drawings by the Old Masters, Collection of J. Pierpont Morgan*, 4 vols., London, 1905-1912.

Heawood
Edward Heawood, *Watermarks, Mainly of the 17th and 18th Centuries*, Hilversum, Holland, 1950.

Kurz, *Bolognese Drawings at Windsor*
Otto Kurz, *The Bolognese Drawings of the XVII and XVIII Centuries . . . at Windsor Castle*, London, 1955.

Le Blanc
Ch. Le Blanc, *Manuel de l'amateur d'estampes*, 4 vols., Paris, 1854-1888.

Lugt
Frits Lugt, *Les Marques de collections de dessins et d'estampes . . .*, Amsterdam, 1921.

Lugt S.
Frits Lugt, *Les Marques de collections de dessins et d'estampes . . . Supplément*, The Hague, 1956.

Lugt, *Répertoire des ventes*
Frits Lugt, *Répertoire des catalogues de ventes publiques*, 3 vols., The Hague, 1938-1964.

Mahon, *Carracci*
Bologna, Palazzo dell'Archiginnasio, "Mostra dei Carracci. Disegni," 1956 (exhibition catalogue by Denis Mahon; second edition, revised, 1963).

Malvasia
Carlo Cesare Malvasia, *Felsina pittrice. Vite de' pittori bolognesi*, Giampietro Zanotti, ed., 2 vols., Bologna, 1841.

Mariette, *Abécédario*
Abécédario de P. J. Mariette et autres notes inédites de cet amateur sur les arts et les artistes, Ph. de Chennevières and A. de Montaiglon, ed., 6 vols., "Archives de l'Art Français," II, IV, VI, VIII, X, XII, Paris, 1851-1860.

Metropolitan Museum, *European Drawings*, I
Metropolitan Museum of Art, *European Drawings from the Collection of The Metropolitan Museum of Art*, I, *Italian Drawings*, New York, 1942.

Morgan Library, *Ninth Fellows Report, 1958*, etc.
The Pierpont Morgan Library, Frederick B. Adams, Jr., compiler, *Annual Report to the Fellows of The Pierpont Morgan Library*, 1950 to date.

Parker, *Ashmolean Catalogue*, II
K. T. Parker, *Catalogue of the Drawings in the Ashmolean Museum*, II, *Italian Schools*, Oxford, 1956.

Vasari Society
The Vasari Society for the Reproduction of Drawings by Old Masters, first series, 10 parts, London, 1905–1915; second series, 16 parts, London, 1920–1935.

De Vesme
Alexandre de Vesme, *Le Peintre-graveur italien*, Milan, 1906.

Vivant Denon, *Monuments*
Monuments des arts du dessin chez les peuples tant anciens que modernes, recueillis par le baron Vivant Denon . . . , décrits et expliqués par Amaury Duval, 4 vols., Paris, 1829.

Voss
Hermann Voss, *Die Malerei des Barock in Rom*, Berlin, 1924.

Witt Collection, *Hand-List*
Hand-List of the Drawings in the Witt Collection, Courtauld Institute of Art, London University, London, 1956.

Exhibitions Cited in an Abbreviated Form

Columbia, S. C., Scholz Exhibition, 1961
   Columbia, South Carolina, Columbia Museum of Art, "Italian Baroque Drawings from the Janos Scholz Collection," 1961.

Dayton, Genoese Masters, 1962–1963
   Dayton, Dayton Art Institute / Sarasota, John and Mable Ringling Museum of Art / Hartford, Wadsworth Atheneum, "Genoese Masters. Cambiaso to Magnasco, 1550–1750," 1962–1963.

Detroit, Italy 1600–1700, 1965
   Detroit, Detroit Institute of Arts, "Art in Italy, 1600–1700," 1965.

Hagerstown, Scholz Exhibition, 1960–1961
   Hagerstown, Maryland, Washington County Museum of Fine Arts, "Four Centuries of Italian Drawings from the Scholz Collection," 1960–1961.

Hamburg, Scholz Exhibition, 1963
   Hamburg, Kunsthalle / Cologne, Wallraf-Richartz Museum, "Italienische Meisterzeichnungen vom 14. bis zum 18. Jahrhundert aus amerikanischem Besitz. Die Sammlung Janos Scholz, New York," 1963.

London, Royal Academy, Italian Art, 1930: commemorative drawings catalogue, 1931

London, Royal Academy of Arts, Burlington House, "Italian Art," 1930 (A. E. Popham, *Italian Drawings Exhibited at the Royal Academy, Burlington House, London, 1930*, London, 1931).

New Haven, Scholz Exhibition, 1964
   New Haven, Yale University Art Gallery, "Italian Drawings from the Collection of Janos Scholz," 1964.

New York, Finch College, Genoese Painters, 1964–1965
   New York, Finch College Museum of Art, "Genoese Painters, Cambiaso to Magnasco, 1550–1750," 1964–1965.

New York, Morgan Library, Landscape Drawings, 1953
   New York, The Pierpont Morgan Library, "Landscape Drawings & Water-colors, Bruegel to Cézanne," 1953.

Oakland, Scholz Exhibition, 1957
   Oakland, Mills College Art Gallery, "Drawings from Bologna, 1520–1800," 1957.

Oakland, Scholz Exhibition, 1961
   Oakland, Mills College Art Gallery, "Drawings from Tuscany and Umbria, 1350–1700," 1961.

Catalogue

Jacopo Chimenti, called
Jacopo da Empoli

Florence 1551–Florence 1640

1 Young Man Seen from the Back

Red chalk, stumped. 16 × 10⅝₆ inches (40.7 × 26.2 cm.). Lined.

Inscribed in pen and brown ink at lower left, *Empoli*.

In this impressive study from life, the draughtsman's attention was focused on the modeling and lighting of the firmly muscled back of the supple figure, which he rendered with the stump in effective contrast to the free rhythms of the strokes that define the drapery. At the same time, the drawing is more than a direct academic statement of the model in its mood of pensive calm. Traditionally, the drawing has been assigned to Jacopo da Empoli, with whose style it presents affinities, particularly in the freer, open passages, but, as Philip Pouncey has recently observed, the weight and substance of the figure, the emphasis on the finish of the modeling, are not wholly characteristic of the Florentine draughtsman. Perhaps, as he maintains, the possibility of a Bolognese origin for the drawing should not be dismissed.

PROVENANCE: Robert Udney (Lugt 2248); Sir Charles Greville (Lugt 549); Earls of Warwick (Lugt 2600); Charles Fairfax Murray; purchased by J. Pierpont Morgan in London, 1910.

BIBLIOGRAPHY: Fairfax Murray, IV, no. 172, repr.

The Pierpont Morgan Library
No. IV, 172

Camillo Procaccini

Bologna 1551(?)–Milan 1629

2 The Martyrdom of a Female Saint

Black chalk, heightened with white, on brownish paper; some ruled lines in pen and brown ink. 18³⁄₁₆ × 12¼ inches (46.2 × 31.1 cm.). Pasted correction at left (including figure of soldier); drawing repaired and extended at right half of lower margin. Upper corners cut to shape of arch. Lined.

An exceptionally highly finished example of the draughtsmanship of Camillo Procaccini, a Bolognese painter who was active and influential in Lombardy. The carefully elaborated narrative, the mannered gestures and elaborate draperies of the figures, and the intricate network of white highlights are all typical of Camillo. The elegance of his style is Emilian, but in this dramatic scene he reveals his debt to the Venetian Pordenone, whose powerful frescoes in S. Maria di Campagna at Piacenza were certainly familiar to him. Although it cannot be related to a surviving picture, this scene of martyrdom devised by Camillo Procaccini was known to at least one contemporary, the Cremonese Giovanni Battista Trotti, who adapted and reversed the composition in a drawing at Christ Church, Oxford (Inv. 1344), where an old inscription identifies the subject as the Martyrdom of St. Euphemia. It was Philip Pouncey who attributed the present drawing to Procaccini and the Oxford drawing to Trotti.

PROVENANCE: Michael Jaffé, Cambridge, England; sale, London, Sotheby's, November 11, 1965, no. 53, repr., bought by the Metropolitan Museum.

EXHIBITIONS: London, Alpine Club Gallery, "Old Master Drawings Presented by W. R. Jeudwine," 1955, no. 49, repr.; London, P. & D. Colnaghi, "Old Master Drawings," 1956, no. 8.

The Metropolitan Museum of Art
Rogers Fund, 65.223

Cristofano Roncalli

Pomarance (near Volterra) 1552–Rome 1626

3 The Holy Family with Angels

Black chalk, heightened with white, on faded blue paper. 14³⁄₁₆ × 10⅝ inches (36.1 × 26.9 cm.). Verso rubbed with black chalk.

Inscribed on verso in pencil, *Parmigiano*.

Study for a *Holy Family* by Roncalli now in the Borghese Gallery, as Philip Pouncey was the first to point out. The drawing comes close to the picture, though the angle of the Virgin's head is considerably altered, and the putto hovering with a crown above the head of the Virgin in the picture is hardly visible here. Another study, in red and white chalks on blue paper, for the Borghese *Holy Family* is in the Uffizi (15428 F., mistakenly attributed to Gabbiani). The long-limbed twisting figures, enveloped in noble but somewhat inflated draperies, and the conservative black chalk style that looks back to Sebastiano del Piombo and Muziano, are characteristic of Roncalli's maturity. He is an artist who bridges two centuries, and though heir to a declining Roman mannerist tradition was a painter of sufficient power and originality to attract the interest of Rubens.

PROVENANCE: Hugh N. Squire, London; purchased by the Metropolitan Museum in London, 1962.

BIBLIOGRAPHY: Philip Pouncey, "Two Drawings by Roncalli," *Burlington Magazine*, XCIV, 1952, p. 356, fig. 70; the Borghese picture fig. 65.

The Metropolitan Museum of Art
Gustavus A. Pfeiffer Fund, 62.120.4

Ludovico Carracci

Bologna 1555–Bologna 1619

4 *The Last Communion of St. Jerome*

Pen and brown ink, brown wash, over traces of black chalk; squared in red chalk. 16⅜ × 11⅞ inches (41.5 × 29 cm.). Repairs at lower left corner; small brown spots at center. The surface of the sheet has suffered from abrasion or dampness. Lined.

It was Ludovico's cousin Agostino Carracci who received the commission to paint for the Bolognese church of S. Girolamo della Certosa the *Last Communion of St. Jerome*, a celebrated, certainly influential picture now in the Bologna Pinacoteca, but both Ludovico and Annibale Carracci seem to have made a try at obtaining this important assignment. Malvasia (I, p. 284) tells us that Annibale supplied a design for the projected picture, and Ludovico, who in 1592 painted a *Baptist Preaching* that was hung opposite Agostino's *Last Communion*, may have made the present drawing in competition with his cousins. Donald Posner has published a drawing in the Louvre as a study by Ludovico for the Certosa *St. Jerome* (*Paragone*, XI, no. 131, 1960, p. 53, pl. 38a), but his attribution has been questioned by Roseline Bacou and Denis Mahon, for whom the drawing is one of Annibale's sketches for the Certosa commission (Paris, Musée du Louvre, "Dessins des Carrache," 1961, p. 16). The present drawing, though unfortunately somewhat

damaged, seems unmistakably to be the work of Ludovico. His manner is apparent in the facial types and in the supple pen line, and these characteristics may also be observed in the Louvre drawing. In Agostino's stately and rather static picture the kneeling St. Jerome receives the last rites in a setting of classical architecture, with a glimpse of landscape beyond. Ludovico here proposes a more animated and informal solution, with a crowd of onlookers gathered in the saint's study. In the Louvre drawing, which is narrower in format, the action takes place against a background of classical columns; below, St. Jerome is seen communing, and above he is carried up to heaven by angels.

PROVENANCE: Unidentified collector (Lugt 1156); purchased by the Metropolitan Museum in London, 1965.

EXHIBITIONS: London, Alpine Club Gallery, "Old Master Drawings Presented by Yvonne ffrench," 1965, no. 12, repr.

The Metropolitan Museum of Art
Rogers Fund, 65.111.1

Agostino Carracci

Bologna 1557–Parma 1602

5 *Portrait of a Woman*

Red chalk on buff paper. 13⅝ × 9¾ inches (34.7 × 24.9 cm.). A number of small losses; brown stain near right margin; black chalk additions in hair. Lined.

A. E. Popham, in cataloguing the Skippe collection prior to its sale at Christie's in 1958, followed for this drawing the ascription to Agostino Carracci that John Skippe himself had penciled on the mat, perhaps around 1800, when he began to mount his collection. Mr. Popham's comment, "a fine original drawing no doubt rightly attributed to Agostino," still stands. Singularly unsparing in its candor, this strong likeness of a woman, her plainness of countenance only slightly relieved by the blossoms tucked in her braids and the ghost of a smile playing about her mouth, is an unforgettable portrait. The painstaking manner in which the planes of the face are modeled by generous areas of regular hatching conforms to the accepted norm of

Agostino's style. The same strict frontality of pose and directness of gaze are found in Agostino's portrait of Giovanna Parolini Guicciardini, a painting in the Staatliche Museen, Berlin-Dahlem, signed and dated 1598 (repr. "Mostra dei Carracci, I Dipinti," Bologna, 1956, pl. 46). For a comparable example in sculpture of this rare kind of frank female portraiture, see the bronze bust of an old woman with braids in the Chicago Art Institute (repr. *Scritti . . . in onore di Mario Salmi*, III, Rome, 1963, p. 45, fig. 4).

PROVENANCE: Jonathan Richardson Junior (Lugt 2170); John Skippe; his descendants, the Martin family, including Mrs. A. D. Rayner-Wood; Edward Holland Martin; Skippe sale, London, Christie's, November 20–21, 1958, no. 63, pl. 9.

EXHIBITIONS: London, Royal Academy of Arts, "Seventeenth Century Art in Europe," 1938, no. 372; New York University, Institute of Fine Arts, "Master Drawings, XVI–XX Century, from the Collection of Curtis O. Baer," 1962, no. 7.

Curtis O. Baer

6 *Woodland and Stream*

Pen and brown ink. 8 1/16 × 11 3/8 inches (20.4 × 28.9 cm.). Small repaired semicircular loss at lower margin center.

Inscribed in pen and brown ink at lower left, *Agosti*; on verso in another hand, *di man[o] d'Agustino Carraccio.*

No one has questioned the traditional attribution of this finished landscape composition, which is based on the old inscriptions on recto and verso. The attribution is further vouched for by the vigorous, even rhythms of the accomplished *facture*, which is that of a draughtsman who was also a printmaker. Its foliage conventions are very much those of the trees in Agostino's print *Apollo and the Python* (Bartsch, XVIII, p. 106, no. 122, as *Perseus and the Dragon*), which records a scene from the Florentine Intermezzi of 1589.

PROVENANCE: Possibly Alfonso IV d'Este (Lugt 106); Charles Fairfax Murray; purchased by J. Pierpont Morgan in London, 1910.

BIBLIOGRAPHY: Fairfax Murray, I, no. 96, repr.

EXHIBITIONS: New York, Morgan Library, Landscape Drawings, 1953, no. 12, pl. 4.

*The Pierpont Morgan Library
No. I, 96*

7 *Landscape with Icarus and Daedalus*

Pen and brown ink over black chalk indications. 10 5/8 × 7 1/8 inches (27 × 18.1 cm.). Light brown stain at upper right corner. Lined with linen.

Numbered in pen and brown ink at lower left, *15*; inscribed at lower right, *Icaro e Dedalo*; on verso of lining in pen and brown ink, *Tintoretti/130*; in pencil at lower left, *Carracci/ 23/S/2.*

The names of both Agostino and Annibale Carracci have been proposed for the authorship of this drawing. Its subject immediately recalls that among the small side-wall frescoes of the Farnese Gallery, which were executed by Annibale Carracci's pupils after their ailing master's sketches, there is a representation of the same episode (repr. John Rupert Martin, *The Farnese Gallery*, Princeton, 1965, fig. 92). The drawing, however, bears no relation to the fresco, where two boatmen dominate the scene, and Daedalus and Icarus are only distant birdlike images. Neither does it have any stylistic affinity with Annibale's surviving pen sketches in the Louvre and at Windsor (repr. Martin, figs. 261–267) that guided his assistants in the execution of the side-wall frescoes. Its Carraccesque character is nevertheless undeniable, particularly in the fine landscape. The present owner acquired the drawing under Agostino's name, and it is left there with a certain logic if not absolute conviction.

BIBLIOGRAPHY: Advertising supplement, *Burlington Magazine*, XCVII, December 1955, pl. x (with text); H. M. Calmann [*Catalogue of Drawings*], London [1960], no. 8, repr.

EXHIBITIONS: New York University, Institute of Fine Arts, "Master Drawings, XVI–XX Century, from the Collection of Curtis O. Baer," 1962, no. 9.

Curtis O. Baer

Ludovico Cardi, called Ludovico Cigoli

Castelvecchio (Tuscany) 1559–Rome 1613

8 *Study for a Figure of Christ*

Brush and brown wash, heightened with white, on paper tinted pink. 10 7/8 × 15 15/16 inches (27.5 × 40.6 cm.). Large repaired loss of lower right corner; small repaired loss at lower left corner; water stains at upper right. Lined.

Inscribed in pen and brown ink on large repair in Richardson's hand, *Andrea Sacchi/Le Poussin*; Richardson numbers on verso of lining.

A fine example of Cigoli's fluent manner of drawing with the brush on a colored ground, the present sheet is a preparatory study for the reclining figure of Christ in the *Feast in the House of Simon*, a signed painting dated 1596, now in the Galleria Doria Pamphili, Rome. The work was commissioned in 1592 by Girolamo Mercuriale of Forlì (1530–1606), professor and doctor of medicine in Bologna and Pisa, who on occasion was called to Vienna to attend Maximilian II. Mercuriale had spent some time in Rome as a student of antiquity, and Baldinucci supposed that it was he who prescribed that the company of diners be represented in the reclining poses of the Roman triclinium. In this connection the sheet embodying the first idea for the composition, acquired by the National Gallery of Canada in 1963, may be particularly significant; it shows Christ and the apostle next to him conventionally seated at table rather than reclining (A. E. Popham and K. M. Fenwick, *The National Gallery of Canada: Catalogue of European Drawings*, Toronto, 1965, no. 319). Patron and artist must have both been familiar with Luke 7:36–50, the biblical passage illustrated by the painting, which in the Vulgate version begins, "Now one of the Pharisees asked Him to dine with him; so He went into the house of the Pharisee and reclined at table."

In addition to the Morgan study and the early sketch in Canada, there are several other drawings connected in one way or another with the Doria painting. There is a squared preparatory drawing for the full composition in the Albertina, and studies for individual figures in the Uffizi and the Louvre, possibly also at Windsor. At Hamburg there is a drawing dated 1597 and therefore presumably made after the painting by Cigoli himself for the use of Cornelis Galle II, who engraved the subject. Carlo Dolci, as Baldinucci noted (*Notizie*, XVIII, pp. 113 ff.), made use of this engraving for his painting of the subject, taking over the triclinium and the pose of the Christ.

Ludovico Cardi, called Cigoli after the place of his birth near Pisa, was active as both painter and architect. Like many Florentine artists of the period, he was more gifted as a draughtsman than as a painter, but the measure of his contemporary fame as a painter may be judged by the fact that his composition of the *Ecce Homo*, now in the Pitti Gallery, Florence, was preferred to that of Caravaggio, and also to that of Passignano, in the competition arranged by Monsignor de' Massimi in 1606.

PROVENANCE: Jonathan Richardson Senior (Lugt 2184); sale, London, Sotheby's, December 1, 1964, no. 22, repr., bought by the Morgan Library.

BIBLIOGRAPHY: Rolf Kultzen, "Mitteilungen aus dem Hamburger Kupferstichkabinett," *Jahrbuch der Hamburger Kunstsammlungen*, X, 1965, p. 186, note 12; Morgan Library, *Fourteenth Fellows Report*, 1965–1966, pp. 109–110.

The Pierpont Morgan Library
Gift of the Fellows, 1964.17

Annibale Carracci
Bologna 1560–Rome 1609

9 *The Monster Cacus*

Black chalk, heightened with white, on faded blue paper. 15 × 19⅜ inches (38.1 × 49.6 cm.). Vertical creases at center; scattered oil and water stains and repairs. Lined with canvas.

Study for the figure of Cacus in a fresco representing Hercules slaying the brigand monster, painted by Annibale Carracci on a chimney in the Palazzo Sampieri-Talon in Bologna. Annibale, his brother Agostino, and his cousin Ludovico all worked in this palace about 1593–1594, decorating three rooms for the Abbate di S. Pietro. The room containing Annibale's chimney fresco with Hercules and Cacus has a ceiling fresco by Agostino representing Hercules helping Atlas support the world. Annibale's fresco in this room has been occasionally attributed to Ludovico or to Agostino, but the style of this preparatory drawing as well as the execution of the fresco testify to Annibale's authorship. Acquired by its present owner as the work of Rubens, and said to be a study for that painter's *Fall of the Rebel Angels* in Munich, the drawing was restored to Annibale and identified as a study for the Palazzo Sampieri-Talon by Michael Jaffé. The vigorous abbreviated chalk modeling announces

Annibale's Roman style, seen at its best in the figure studies for the Farnese Gallery. Domenichino borrowed this figure of a monster from Annibale, utilizing it in his early lunette-shaped fresco representing the Temptation of St. Jerome in the portico of S. Onofrio al Gianicolo, Rome (repr. Evelina Borea, *Domenichino*, Milan, 1965, pl. 4).

BIBLIOGRAPHY: Michael Jaffé, "Some Drawings by the Carracci," *Paragone*, VII, no. 83, 1956, pp. 12–13, pl. 4; Julius S. Held, *Rubens, Selected Drawings*, I, London, 1959, p. 113 (as Rubens); Michael Jaffé, "The Master Hand of Rubens" (review of Held's book), *Art News*, LVIII, 1959, p. 62; Claus Virch, *Master Drawings in the Collection of Walter C. Baker*, New York, 1962 [privately printed], no. 26, repr.

EXHIBITIONS: Poughkeepsie, Vassar College/New York, Wildenstein, "Centennial Loan Exhibition. Drawings and Watercolors from Alumnae and their Families," 1961, no. 27, repr.

Walter C. Baker

10 *Landscape with Jacob Sleeping*

Pen and brown ink, brown wash, over slight traces of black chalk. 16¼ × 10⁵⁄₁₆ inches (41.3 × 26.2 cm.). Repairs at upper margin and at lower right; crease at right corner.

Inscribed in pen and brown ink at lower margin, *di mano di Anniballe Carracci*; numbered at upper right corner, *2*; inscribed on the old mount (now detached from the drawing), *Jacob asleep, y.ᵃ ladder with the angels at a great distance.*

But for the light indication, added perhaps as an afterthought, of a ladder rising up to heaven in the background, which identifies the sleeping youth as Jacob, this delightful drawing could be treated as a pure landscape. The verticality of the composition and the predominance given to the foreground place the sheet among Annibale's Bolognese experiments in landscape; his later Roman landscapes were broader, more logically constructed, and they set the example for classic seventeenth-century landscape painting. Another version of this composition with a youth asleep at the foot of a clump of trees, but without the ladder and with considerable variations, is in the Ellesmere collection; this sheet is dated 1595 (repr. Mahon, pl. 113).

PROVENANCE: Sir Peter Lely (Lugt 2092); Earls of Pembroke; Pembroke sale, London, Sotheby's, July 5–10, 1917, no. 376, bought by the Metropolitan Museum.

BIBLIOGRAPHY: S. Arthur Strong, *Reproductions in Facsimile of Drawings by the Old Masters in the Collection of the Earl of Pembroke and Montgomery at Wilton House*, London, 1900, Part V, repr. no. 44; Bryson Burroughs, "Drawings among the Recent Accessions," *Metropolitan Museum of Art Bulletin*, August 1919, p. 176, repr.; "Some Italian Drawings in the Metropolitan Museum," *Connoisseur*, CX, 1943, p. 151, repr.; P. A. Tomory, *The Ellesmere Collection of Old Master Drawings*, Leicester, 1954, p. 26; Mahon, *Carracci*, p. 163.

EXHIBITIONS: Philadelphia Museum of Art, "Masterpieces of Drawing," 1950–1951, no. 47, repr.; New York, Morgan Library, Landscape Drawings, 1953, no. 13; Detroit, Italy 1600–1700, 1965, no. 73, repr.

*The Metropolitan Museum of Art
Hewitt Fund, 19.76.14*

11 *Anteros Victorious*

Red chalk. 8¾ × 6¼ inches (22.2 × 15.9 cm.). Oil stain at top of sheet. Lined.

Inscribed in pen and brown ink at lower left, *annibale Caracci.*

Annibale Carracci's major Roman enterprise was the frescoed decoration of the vault of the Gallery of the Palazzo Farnese, begun in 1597 and finished about 1604. This decoration was conceived as a complex but completely logical interweaving of full-scale, independent painted compositions in simulated frames (*quadri riportati*) and illusionistic architectural painting (*quadratura*). At the four corners of the cove vault of the long gallery the painted architecture opens to reveal triangular glimpses of painted sky, against which are silhouetted pairs of putti standing on balustrades. These putti are combined to represent contrasts between spiritual and sensuous loves, for the theme of the decoration of the Gallery is the Loves of the Gods. In one corner Cupid and Anteros are represented struggling for the palm branch, and a black chalk drawing in the Louvre (Inv. 7305; Mahon, *Carracci*, no. 188) is Annibale's study for this solution. The Metropolitan Museum's drawing represents an earlier stage of the artist's planning for this corner, a stage at which the artist thought of representing the victorious Anteros holding aloft the disputed palm branch and being carried by two putti. Popham has pointed out that the group studied in this drawing is probably based on a composition of three putti lifting up a fourth, engraved as an invention of Parmigianino and also recorded in two pictures attributed to Parmigianino in English collections, one at Knole, the other at Brocklesby Park. Preparatory studies by Annibale for the putti in the three other corners of the Farnese ceiling fresco are at Windsor Castle, the Louvre, Besançon, and in the Ellesmere collection.

PROVENANCE: Lionel Lucas (Lugt S. 1733a); Lucas sale, London, Christie's, December 9, 1949, part of no. 67; Hugh N. Squire, London; purchased by the Metropolitan Museum in London, 1962.

BIBLIOGRAPHY: Michael Jaffé, "The Carracci at Newcastle," *Burlington Magazine*, CIV, 1962, p. 26, fig. 29; J. Bean, *Metropolitan Museum of Art Bulletin*, March 1963, p. 231, repr. cover; Bean, *100 European Drawings*, no. 27, repr.; John Rupert Martin, *The Farnese Gallery*, Princeton, 1965, pp. 229, 270, no. 125, fig. 240; Walter Vitzthum, review of Martin's book, *Master Drawings*, IV, 1966, p. 48, pl. 35.

EXHIBITIONS: London, P. & D. Colnaghi, "Old Master Drawings," 1950, no. 10; Newcastle upon Tyne, King's College, "The Carracci, Drawings and Paintings," 1961, no. 136, pl. XXXVI.

The Metropolitan Museum of Art
Gustavus A. Pfeiffer Fund, 62.120.2

12 *Flying Putto*

Black chalk, stumped. 11⅝ × 7⅛ inches (29.5 × 18.1 cm.). Numerous stains; repaired loss of upper right corner.

Verso: Pen and black ink, black chalk drawing of a similar flying putto.

This rapid rendering of a flying *amoretto* holding a branch or palm is akin in style to certain of the studies for the numerous cupids of the Farnese frescoes, but it does not appear to have been utilized in this project. It is closer to the stumped black chalk studies in the Louvre and at Windsor (repr. John Rupert Martin, *The Farnese Gallery*, Princeton, 1965, figs. 242, 245) than to the previous red chalk study (No. 11).

PROVENANCE: Purchased in Rome.

EXHIBITIONS: Oakland, Scholz Exhibition, 1957, no. 20, repr.; Detroit, Italy 1600–1700, 1965, no. 76, repr.

Janos Scholz

13 *Study of an Angel*

Black chalk, heightened with white, on blue paper. 14 × 9¾ inches (35.5 × 24.8 cm.). Several spots of rose-colored paint at lower left.

Numbered in pen and black ink at lower right corner, *8*.

Verso: Black and white chalk study of a cushion.

In the very first years of the seventeenth century, Cardinal Antonio Maria Salviati commissioned from Annibale Carracci an altarpiece to ornament a chapel in the church of S. Gregorio Magno in Rome. The subject chosen was St. Gregory Praying for the Souls in Purgatory; the saint was represented kneeling, facing the spectator and attended by two youthful angels, one on his knees to the left of the saint, the other standing at the right. Probably begun before the cardinal's death in April 1602, the picture was no doubt finished when the chapel was consecrated in October 1603. From Rome the St. Gregory altarpiece, a majestic work of Annibale's mature Roman style, found its way into the Ellesmere collection at Bridgewater House in London, where unfortunately it was burned during World War II (repr. Voss, p. 181). This drawing, a study from a young model in the studio, with angel wings indicated above his shoulders, was made in preparation for the angel on the right. Annibale has experimented with a number of alternative positions for the angel's right arm and hand, but the final position of the arm in the drawing corresponds quite closely to that detail in the picture. On the verso of the sheet is a study for the cushion on which St. Gregory kneels. Only two other drawings for the St. Gregory altarpiece seem to have survived: an elaborate composition study with many variations at Chatsworth (repr. "Old Master Drawings from Chatsworth," exhibition circulated by the Smithsonian Institution, 1962–1963, pl. 13) and a freer composition study at Windsor Castle (Rudolf Wittkower, *The Drawings of the Carracci . . . at Windsor Castle*, London, 1952, p. 145, no. 351). A third design was once in Vivant Denon's collection (repr. *Monuments*, III, pl. 189).

PROVENANCE: Hugh N. Squire, London; purchased by the Metropolitan Museum in London, 1962.

BIBLIOGRAPHY: Michael Jaffé, "The Carracci at New-castle," *Burlington Magazine*, CIV, 1962, p. 26, fig. 28; J. Bean, *Metropolitan Museum of Art Bulletin*, March 1963, pp. 225–227, repr. frontispiece; Bean, *100 European Drawings*, no. 28, repr.

EXHIBITIONS: Newcastle upon Tyne, King's College, "The Carracci, Drawings and Paintings," 1961, no. 154, pl. XLI.

The Metropolitan Museum of Art
Gustavus A. Pfeiffer Fund, 62.120.1

14 *Shepherd with Pipes, and Two Dancing Children; Virgin and Child with Heads of Four Spectators*

Pen and brown ink. 6⅟₁₆ × 8⅟₁₆ inches (15.3 × 21.7 cm.). Executed on verso of rare proof state of the artist's etching *Christ Crowned with Thorns*, before letters (Bartsch, XVIII, p. 182, no. 3. Etching in later state is inscribed, *Annib. Carracius in. et fecit. 1606*).

This unpublished drawing in the heavily accented manner of Annibale's late drawings is important as a study for the *Adoration of the Shepherds*, a lost painting by the master that inspired a number of copies and variations by his followers. The lost painting is described in detail by Bellori (*Le Vite de' pittori, scultori e architetti . . .*, Rome, 1672, p. 86), who mentions the "pastore in piedi, che suona la cornamusa," the figure studied at the far left of the present drawing. Bellori reported that the original having gone to France, its composition was known through a copy from the hand of Domenichino, a picture now generally assumed to be identical with the *Adoration of the Shepherds* at the Dulwich Gallery. (Domenichino's copy and other variations of Annibale's lost picture by Lanfranco and Sisto Badalocchio are discussed and illustrated by Erich Schleier in the *Burlington Magazine*, CII, 1964, pp. 246–251).

The fact that the present drawing is executed on the verso of a rare proof impression of one of Annibale's etchings, dated 1606 in its final state, makes it possible to place the lost painting more precisely than has hitherto been possible. The *terminus post quem* date of 1606 is considerably later than had been thought probable (see Denis Mahon's essay in the catalogue of the 1961 Carracci exhibition at the Louvre, and Wittkower's remarks under nos. 89, 157, and 344 of his catalogue of the Carracci drawings at Windsor Castle), and we now have evidence that Annibale produced, in addition to some drawings and two etchings, at least one painting following the illness that struck him early in 1605.

The bagpiper in the Dulwich painting depends very heavily on the figure in this drawing although his right instead of left leg bears his weight and the left arm has been lowered to reveal the upper part of the instrument. Possibly a chalk study intervened between this drawing and Annibale's painting. This close affinity between the drawing and the Dulwich painting is further evidence of the faithfulness of Domenichino's copy. The two children who, in the drawing, appear to step to the music of the piper, do not appear in the painting, where there is a further alteration in the shifting of the Child's head to the Virgin's left arm.

Wittkower associated two Windsor drawings with the composition recorded in the Dulwich painting: one by Annibale, which is a black chalk study for the figure of the boy holding a dove (Wittkower, no. 344), and the second, a sheet of studies by Agostino (Wittkower, no. 89) that "repeats motifs" of the Dulwich painting. Some difficulty arises in the case of the second sheet, since Agostino, who died in 1602, could not have known Annibale's *Adoration of the Shepherds* if, as the present drawing seems to indicate, it was executed in 1606 or later. It is, of course, conceivable but not likely that Annibale's print of the *Ecce Homo* could have been executed some time before it received his signature and the date 1606.

Private Collection

Annibale Carracci or Studio

Bologna 1560–Rome 1609

15 *Album of Drawings: The Life of St. Paul*

Forty-nine folios including two frontispieces, a title page lettered *VITA/DI SAN PAOLO APOSTOLO/REPPRESENTATA IN DISSEGNO/ET DICCHIARATA/*

IN SCRITTO, and forty-six pages of illustrations, each with a page of manuscript text in Italian to the left numbered I to XLVI. Pen and brown ink, wash in varying shades of brown, occasionally in gray, over light indications in leadpoint. Watermarks: heraldic mountain composed of three hills surmounted by an F, within a shield (Briquet 11938), fragmented, on 22 folios; H within a circle (?), fragment, folio 1; star within a shield, fragment, folio 2. Bound in an eighteenth-century Italian binding of brown morocco, with narrow gold-tooled borders and spine, the latter with the title label in black (*DESEGE / DI / N. POUSSI.*). Binding: 11 × 8¼ inches (28 × 21 cm.); folio: 10⅝ × 8¼ inches (27 × 20.9 cm.).

Inscribed on verso of flyleaf in pencil in a nineteenth-century hand, *Mr. Lyon's Friend*; on folio 2, in pen and brown ink, in an older hand, *Illmo Sig^re Pron Col^mo*; in another old hand, *Auuocato*; *Auacotos*; also various scribbles in a child's hand.

Folio 1. *Frontispiece, I*
Folio 33. *Paul Preaching to Felix and Drusilla*

This interesting, little-known album of drawings was first linked with Annibale Carracci by J. Byam Shaw when it appeared on the London art market in 1964, described at that time only as "Italian, early seventeenth century." Those scholars who have since seen the album have concurred in the association with Annibale Carracci but with varying degrees of conviction as to whether or not the drawings are from the hand of the master himself or that of a member of his studio. Several Carracci students have voiced their concurrence in Byam Shaw's belief that the execution is Annibale's own; Walter Vitzthum, thus far the only scholar whose conclusions have been recorded in print, speaks of the album as belonging "to the same late phase of Annibale's studio" as the Stockholm drawings that relate to the frescoes executed for the Herrera Chapel of S. Giacomo degli Spagnuoli, Rome, between 1602 and 1607. Comparison of the drawings of the St. Paul cycle with the *Adoration of the Shepherds* in the exhibition (No. 14), appears to underscore the validity of Mr. Vitzthum's conclusion. If, as seems indisputable, the *Adoration of the Shepherds* is to be taken as an example of Annibale's late manner, with its varying pressures of the pen and tendency to revise contours, the more uniform penwork of the album may bespeak a disciple's hand, possibly, as in the instance of the Herrera drawings, a hand working in translation of the master's ideas. The variety and authority of invention are notable throughout the album.

The purpose for which the album was made is conjectural. Was it meant for private devotional use or instruction, or as a model for an illustrated book? Was it perhaps an elaborate program of designs for an extensive painting commission? Its two intricate frontispieces each contain Latin phrases from the texts of the apostle Paul, combined more or less in rebus form with small emblems and devices displayed on a monumental arch. Through the arch a scene from the saint's life is visible; in the folio here illustrated as pl. 15, it is the miracle following Paul's beheading, when springs burst forth at the three points where his severed head rebounded. Illustration XLV of the album is also devoted to this subject. The manuscript text opposite each illustration contains the relevant biblical passage, in each instance properly identified in the margin as to its source in the books of Acts, Corinthians, etc. A. L. Gabriel points out that *An. Chr.*, followed by various numerals, which appears on each page, is the abbreviation of *Anno Christi*, i.e., the Christian year in which the event described presumably took place. No evidence has been found to associate this cycle of illustrations of the life of the apostle Paul with the pontificate of Pope Paul V (1605–1621).

The album owes its old title *Desege di N. Poussi.* to the fact that until recently a letter dated Paris, June 13, 1642, from Nicolas Poussin to his patron Cassiano dal Pozzo was preserved with it. The letter, which was published by G. Bottari (*Raccolta di lettere sulla pittura scultura e d'architettura . . .*, I, Rome, 1754, p. 295) was sold separately (Sotheby's, March 16, 1964, no. 249).

PROVENANCE: Mrs. Allan Cameron; sale, London, Sotheby's, March 11, 1964, no. 156, repr. (frontispiece and illustration XIV).

BIBLIOGRAPHY: Walter Vitzthum, review, "Italienska Barockteckningar," *Master Drawings*, III, 1965, p. 412; Morgan Library, *Fourteenth Fellows Report, 1965–1966*, pp. 111–113, folio 20, repr.

The Pierpont Morgan Library
Gift of the Fellows, 1964.9

Belisario Corenzio

Naples about 1560–Naples about 1640

16 *Joshua Stopping the Sun*

Brush, gray and blue wash, heightened with white, over a little black chalk, on light brown paper. 8¾ × 10¼ inches (22.3 × 26.1 cm.). All four corners trimmed. Partially lined.

Inscribed in pen and brown ink at lower left, *Bellisario*; on verso in pen and brown ink, *Gius . . . d'Arpino.*

A particularly attractive example of Corenzio's brush style in drawing, identified by Vitzthum as a study for one of the artist's frescoes in the vault of the western arm of the Gesù Nuovo in Naples, a church built on the plan of a Greek cross. The same scholar has convincingly suggested that the artist's lavish use of colored wash and white highlights had its origin in Venice, where Corenzio is said to have worked in Tintoretto's studio before he came to Naples. The stylistic parallels with Domenico Tintoretto's brush drawings are indeed striking. Corenzio decorated a great many Neapolitan churches, and he was as prolific a draughtsman as a painter. Other New York collections, the Cooper Union and the Metropolitan Museum, possess characteristic sheets by him.

BIBLIOGRAPHY: Walter Vitzthum, "Neapolitan Seicento Drawings in Florida," *Burlington Magazine*, CIII, 1961, p. 313, fig. 21.

EXHIBITIONS: Sarasota, The Ringling Museums, "Baroque Painters of Naples," 1961, no. 47, repr.; Columbia, S. C., Scholz Exhibition, 1961, no. 27.

Janos Scholz

Giovanni Battista Caracciolo

Naples 1570–Naples 1637

17 *David with the Head of Goliath*

Pen and brown ink, brown wash. 10¹¹⁄₁₆ × 7¹³⁄₁₆ inches (27.1 × 19.8 cm.). Lower right corner replaced; brown stains at upper left and at right margin. Watermark: three superimposed circles surmounted by a cross.

Verso: Part of a shopping list in Spanish, in pen and brown ink, irrelevant to the drawing.

Drawings by Caracciolo, a powerful and original Neapolitan master who profited richly from the example of Caravaggio, are rare, and this fine sheet is, to our knowledge, the only sample of his draughtsmanship to be found in an American collection. Typical of Caracciolo is David's strikingly large oval head with its broad nose and mouth; the same facial type occurs not only in the artist's pictures, but as well in other drawings traditionally attributed to him. In a study of three seated youths in the Louvre (repr. Nicola Ivanoff, *I Disegni italiani del seicento. Scuola veneta, lombarda, ligure, napoletana*, Venice [1959], pl. 80), from the collection of P.-J. Mariette, who recorded the attribution to Caracciolo, we encounter the same physical type, and a transposition into black chalk of the vigorous pen and brush line of the present drawing. It is impossible to say if Caracciolo, or any other artist for that matter, was influenced by the draughtsmanship of Caravaggio, for no drawings by that master seem to have survived; on the other hand, Caracciolo's pen style is clearly related to that of his teacher, Fabrizio Santafede.

PROVENANCE: Giovanni Piancastelli (no mark, see Lugt S. 2078a); Mr. and Mrs. Edward Brandegee (no mark, see Lugt S. 1860c).

BIBLIOGRAPHY: Walter Vitzthum, review of Detroit exhibition, *Master Drawings*, III, no. 4, 1965, pp. 407–408.

EXHIBITIONS: Detroit, Italy 1600–1700, 1965, no. 147, repr.

Janos Scholz

Guido Reni

Calvenzano (Bologna) 1575–Bologna 1642

18 *Sketches of Putti*

Pen and brown ink. 6 × 8³⁄₁₆ inches (15.2 × 20.8 cm.), sight.

Verso: Pen and brown ink studies for the *Madonna della Pietà*, and a black chalk study for *Lucretia*.

Mrs. Krautheimer published a detailed analysis of her double-sided sheet in the 1962 *Burlington*, noting that the connection of its recto with the monochrome frescoes in S. Maria dei Servi, Bologna, was first recognized by Otto Kurz. The pairs of *angelotti* winging across the face of the sheet embody the variations and mutations with which Reni, in his usual fashion, experimented before settling on

the final design for the frescoes of the pairs of putti
—each fitted into a cruciform space, one duo supporting a mitre and the other a crozier—that flank
the figure of S. Carlo Borromeo in the vault of the
Capella di Giovanni Francesco dall'Armi, the
eighth chapel on the left at S. Maria dei Servi. The
final preparatory studies that must have preceded
the execution of the frescoes are not known. Since
it is generally assumed that the frescoes were ready
for the dedication of the chapel in 1612, they are
customarily dated 1611–1612, although the possibility is not ruled out, as Mrs. Krautheimer noted,
that they might have been executed after the dedication.

Mrs. Krautheimer argues that the chalk sketch
of the seated female figure on the verso is a first
thought for the *Lucretia* (versions in the Neues
Schloss, Potsdam and the Galleria Spada, Rome),
and she makes a plausible case for the rapid pen
sketches as germinal ideas for the *Madonna della
Pietà*, Pinacoteca, Bologna.

PROVENANCE: H. Gilhofer and H. Ranschburg, Lucerne
(*Lager Katalog No. 19* [1930s], no. 28); purchased in New
York, 1961.

BIBLIOGRAPHY: Trude Krautheimer-Hess, "A Sheet of
Sketches by Guido Reni," *Burlington Magazine*, CIV, 1962,
pp. 385–386, figs. 28–29.

Mrs. Richard Krautheimer

19 Solomon's Idolatry

Pen and brown ink, brown wash, over red chalk. 14 3/16 ×
21 7/16 inches (36 × 54.5 cm.). Water stain along left margin;
vertical crease through center. Lined.

Inscribed in pen and brown ink at lower left, *Guido*; partially obliterated old numbers in pen and brown ink on
verso of lining.

In this carefully composed, finished drawing, Reni
depicts Solomon in his old age with his "strange
wives" and concubines sacrificing to one of the
gods to which they had "turned away his heart"
(I Kings 11:4–8). The large design was most likely
made with a fresco or painting in view, and Stephen
Pepper has called attention to G. Campori's listing
of "Un Quadro dell'Idolatria di Salomone, di
Guido" from a collection sold in Bologna in the
seventeenth century (*Raccolti di cataloghi ed inven-*

tarii inediti, Modena, 1870, p. 431). Stylistically, the
drawing is not far removed from the Windsor and
Chatsworth drawings for the frescoes of the Cappella Paolina of S. Maria Maggiore, Rome, 1610–
1612, and the first sketches of 1613 in the Palazzo
Bianco, Genoa (repr. *Jahrbuch der Kunsthistorischen
Sammlungen in Wien*, N. F., XI, 1937, pp. 204–205)
for the *Madonna della Pietà*, now in the Pinacoteca,
Bologna, but originally installed on the high altar
of the Chiesa dei Mendicanti, Bologna, in 1616.
The Morgan drawing may well date from the same
period.

The subject of Solomon's Idolatry is compara-
tively rare. It was represented by Pietro da Cortona
in the Palazzo Mattei, Rome (see Briganti, *Cortona*,
pp. 161–163, pl. 16; see also No. 53 of the exhibition).

PROVENANCE: Nathaniel Hone (Lugt 2793); Paul Sandby
(Lugt 2112); Sir Thomas Lawrence (Lugt 2445); Sale of a
Well-known Amateur [Hope, according to Lugt, *Réper-
toire des ventes*; Brooke, according to the Fairfax Murray
Notebooks], London, Sotheby's, June 20, 1891, no. 219;
Charles Fairfax Murray; purchased by J. Pierpont Morgan
in London, 1910.

BIBLIOGRAPHY: Fairfax Murray, IV, no. 163, repr.

*The Pierpont Morgan Library
No. IV, 163*

20 Torso: Study for Christ on the Cross

Black and white chalk, with a few strokes of red chalk, on
gray paper. 14 5/8 × 9 15/16 inches (37.1 × 25.2 cm.). Several oil
stains.

Inscribed on verso of an old lining, apparently trimmed,
in pen and brown ink, *Guido Reni per il Crocifisso dei Cap-
pucini di Bologna uno dei più*.

The phrase "Praxitelean beauty," which Otto Kurz
used in speaking of Guido Reni's art, is especially
descriptive of this sensitive study of a lithe male
torso. Full of grace, it is also fully authoritative
anatomically, and it conveys a suggestion of the
pathos of the subject for which the figure was ultimately intended. The drawing is a study for the
Crucifixion from the church of the Capuchin Friars,
now in the Pinacoteca at Bologna, the first of
Reni's paintings of the subject, which Kurz (*Jahrbuch der Kunsthistorischen Sammlungen in Wien*,
N. F., XI, 1937, p. 216), followed by Cavalli (C.

Gnudi and G. C. Cavalli, *Guido Reni*, Florence, 1955, no. 37, pl. 74), dated around 1616. The relationship with the painting, first noted when the sheet entered the Morgan Library, was further confirmed when the heavy lining of the drawing was removed to reveal, on the remnant of an even earlier lining, the inscription cited above.

Kurz in his article on Guido Reni mentioned that there was a preparatory drawing in black chalk for the figure of the Virgin in the Capuchin *Crucifixion* on the art market in Berlin in 1931 (*Second Catalogue of Drawings by the Old Masters*, Karl E. Maison, Viktoria-Strasse 33, Berlin [unpaged]). Mr. Maison kindly reports that the drawing was sold again in an anonymous sale at Gutekunst and Klipstein, Berne, on November 22, 1956 (no. 257 of the catalogue where it was noted that the sheet was at one time in the collection of Dr. M. K. H. Rech). It was acquired by Dr. W. Berndt at the 1956 sale, but it has not been possible to ascertain its present whereabouts. The drawing of a thorn-crowned head of Christ in the Louvre (Inv. 8902. Black and red chalk on light brown paper, 31.5 × 25.6 cm.), while a more highly finished drawing than the Morgan sheet, may possibly be a study for the head of the Christ in the Bologna picture. The *Hand-List* of the Witt Collection (p. 85, no. 2412) associates a red and white chalk "study of a draped female figure, and a study of the head" with the *Crucifixion*. According to Walter Vitzthum, the red chalk study of a torso in the Kunsthalle, Bremen, is also related to this famous painting although the pose differs somewhat.

PROVENANCE: Count Moriz von Fries (Lugt 2903); Marquis de Lagoy (Lugt 1710); probably Thomas Dimsdale; Sir Thomas Lawrence (Lugt 2445); purchased by the Morgan Library in London, 1961.

BIBLIOGRAPHY: Morgan Library, *Eleventh Fellows Report, 1961*, pp. 82–83; Denis Mahon, "Stock-taking in Seicento Studies," *Apollo*, LXXXII, 1965, pp. 384, 386, fig. 7; Walter Vitzthum, review of Detroit exhibition, *Master Drawings*, III, no. 4, 1965, p. 407; Walter Vitzthum, review of "Günter Busch: . . . Handzeichnungen . . . aus dem Besitz der Kunsthalle Bremen," *Master Drawings*, IV, 1966, p. 185.

EXHIBITIONS: Detroit, Italy 1600–1700, 1965, no. 86, repr.

The Pierpont Morgan Library
Gift of the Fellows, 1961.34

21 *The Headless Body of Holofernes*

Black chalk on brownish paper. 15 × 10¼ inches (38.1 × 26.1 cm.). A sketch of a female figure in black chalk on blue paper (7⁷⁄₁₆ × 3⅜ inches, 17.9 × 8.5 cm.) has been pasted down at the lower left of the larger sheet. Lined.

Inscribed in pen and brown ink at lower right, *donatomi dal Sig. Paolo Albertonio scol.º del St.* (?) *Zignani*.

A study, no doubt made from life, for the left arm and shoulder of the headless body of Holofernes in the *Judith and Holofernes* of the Spada Gallery in Rome (repr. Federico Zeri, *La Galleria Spada in Roma*, Florence, 1954, p. 110, no. 97, pl. 146). Zeri dates the picture, in which Judith stands beside the corpse looking up to heaven and holding the head of Holofernes in her left hand, about 1625–1630. The black chalk modeling is somewhat firmer and more "academic" here than in Reni's earlier study of the torso of Christ (No. 20 above). The delicately drawn figure of a half-draped female figure at lower left, also by Reni, is a separate sketch that has been pasted by a collector onto the larger sheet.

PROVENANCE: Paolo Albertonio (according to inscription on sheet); purchased by the Metropolitan Museum in London, 1962.

EXHIBITIONS: London, Alpine Club Gallery, "Old Master and Early English Drawings Presented by Yvonne ffrench," 1962, no. 12, repr.

The Metropolitan Museum of Art
Rogers Fund, 62.123.1

Antonio d'Errico, called Tanzio da Varallo

Riale d'Alagna about 1575–Varallo about 1635

22 *A Group of Soldiers with Pikes*

Red chalk, faint traces of heightening with white (the heightening in white gouache is apparently recent), a few touches of black chalk. 16⁷⁄₁₆ × 11⅝ inches (41.7 × 28.8 cm.). Crease line across center with a break at the right margin; some small stains near lower and upper center. Lined.

The major monument of the Piedmontese town of Varallo in the province of Vercelli is the Franciscan sanctuary of the Sacro Monte. Begun in the late fifteenth century, originally with the idea of creating a new Jerusalem, it now consists of the Basilica of the Assumption and more than forty chapels scattered over the hill. Here the events of the Life and Passion of Christ are depicted in a curious combination of terracotta figures and frescoes, strikingly *trompe-l'oeil* in their fusion. Notable among the generations of artists who have contributed to these dramatic tableaux are Gaudenzio Ferrari, Pellegrino Tibaldi, Morazzone, and Antonio d'Errico, known as Tanzio da Varallo. Tanzio and his brother Giovanni, a sculptor who had done work for Morazzone, were responsible for the decoration of three chapels: Chapel XXVII showing Christ before Pilate (1616–1617), Chapel XXXIV, Pilate Washing his Hands (1618–1620), and Chapel XXVIII, Christ before Herod (completed 1628).

The Morgan drawing is a study for a segment of the frescoes on the walls of this last chapel, peopled by thirty-five of Giovanni d'Errico's realistically sculpted figures (repr. "Mostra di Tanzio da Varallo," Palazzo Madama, Turin, 1959, pls. 68–82 and color pl. VIII). It was recognized by J. Byam Shaw and others when it was sold recently at Christie's with an attribution to Sassoferrato. Done from the model, at least in the case of the two foremost figures, it consciously emphasizes the plastic values and lighting (note the wall shadows) that were vital for the illusionism of the final ensemble. In the fresco, the face of the leading figure, which has the quality of a portrait in the drawing, becomes an anxious, bearded visage; the boy in the rear is given a plumed cap; and another head is added. The leg that is visible between the legs of the leading soldier is obviously a *pentimento*; more curious is the discrepancy in the thigh pieces of the soldier's armor. At least one other drawing for the Herod chapel survives in the Pinacoteca in Varallo (repr. "Mostra di Tanzio da Varallo," pl. 138) where the greater part of Tanzio's drawings are preserved.

BIBLIOGRAPHY: Giovanni Testor, "Una postilla e un inedito," *Paragone*, XVII, no. 199, 1966, pp. 55–56, pl. 51 (as preparatory for Chapel XXVII).

PROVENANCE: B. H. Balfour (inscribed on verso); sale, London, Christie's, March 29, 1966, no. 45, repr. (as Sassoferrato), bought by the Pierpont Morgan Library.

The Pierpont Morgan Library
Gift of the Fellows, 1966.3

Leonello Spada
Bologna 1576–Parma 1622

23 *David with the Head of Goliath*

Pen and brown ink, brown wash, over black chalk indications. 10½ × 6 inches (26.7 × 15.2 cm.). Lined.

Inscribed in pen and brown ink at lower right, extending slightly onto old lining, *Léon Spada le tableau/est dans la galerie du/ Marquis Cospi—Malvasia/a fol 107.*

As a former owner of this drawing (presumably an eighteenth-century Frenchman to judge from his handwriting) was obviously aware, Malvasia in his *Felsina pittrice*, first published in 1678, mentions at least three paintings of David by Spada, two in the gallery of the Marchese Cospi and one in the house of Dr. Luca Antonio Fabbri. The passage to which the inscription on the drawing refers reads: "... teste particolarmente di Daviddi, che colla spada in una mano, coll'altra impugnavano il teschio dell'orgoglioso Golia, due de'quali trovansi oggi nella galleria del sig. Marchese Cospi, e uno in casa del Dottor Luca Antonio Fabbri; siccome una Giuditta, ed un' altra in casa Lupari." Although it is not entirely clear from Malvasia's text whether the description of David—posed with sword in one hand and grasping the head of the proud Goliath with the other—applies to both the Cospi pictures, it seems unlikely that one collector would own two paintings of the selfsame composition. It could well have been that the French owner had specific knowledge of the relationship of his drawing to one of the two pictures—or possibly he linked his sheet with the Malvasia reference merely by reason of the subject. The marchese was presumably a member of the Cospi family of Bologna. In a painting attributed to Spada in the collection of Lord Methuen, Corsham Court, David clasps the giant's head with both hands, but no sword is shown; yet another pose occurs in the painting at Dresden representing David giving the head of Goliath to a soldier.

Although Spada was at one point known in his native Bologna as "Caravaggio's ape," it is his connection with the Carracci circle that prevails in the Manning drawing, both in the figure type and in the manner of execution.

PROVENANCE: D. B. (Lugt S. 729).

EXHIBITIONS: Detroit, Italy 1600–1700, 1965, no. 112, repr.

Robert and Bertina Suida Manning

Giacomo Cavedone

Sassuolo (Modena) 1577–Bologna 1660

24 *Half-Figure of a Woman with Arms Outstretched*

Black chalk, heightened with white, on blue paper. 9⅞ × 14½ inches (25.1 × 36.8 cm.).

Inscribed in pen and brown ink at lower right, *Cavedoni*.

Verso: Red chalk study of legs.

The old inscription *Cavedoni* supplies the correct attribution; this is a fine example of Giacomo Cavedone's chalk style. The heavy draperies, broadly indicated, are typical, as is the simple but solemn pose of the figure, no doubt studied for a mourning Virgin. The drawing may well be a preparatory study for Cavedone's *Deposition* in the Sanctuary of the Madonna at Caravaggio, where the Virgin is seated with arms outspread at the foot of the Cross (repr. *Paragone*, VII, no. 77, 1956, fig. 26).

PROVENANCE: Giovanni Piancastelli (no mark, see Lugt S. 2078a); Mr. and Mrs. Edward Brandegee (no mark, see Lugt S. 1860c).

EXHIBITIONS: Scholz Exhibitions: Oakland, 1957, no. 42, repr.; Hagerstown, 1960–1961, no. 35; Columbia, S.C., 1961, no. 26; Hamburg, 1963, no. 39.

Janos Scholz

Matteo Rosselli

Florence 1578–Florence 1650

25 *Study of an Archer, and Three Studies of His Hands*

Red chalk (for standing figure) and black chalk (for studies of hands). 11 13/16 × 8¼ inches (30 × 21 cm.). Brown stain at lower center.

Verso: Black chalk study of an archer.

A spirited and characteristic figure study by Rosselli, who, like all his Florentine predecessors and contemporaries, drew extensively from the model. His partiality for a soft, rather ornamental line is apparent in his handling of red and black chalk in this drawing, convincingly attributed to Rosselli by Philip Pouncey.

EXHIBITIONS: Scholz Exhibitions: Oakland, 1961, no. 72, repr.; Columbia, S.C., 1961, no. 71, repr.; Hamburg, 1963, no. 140, pl. 29; New Haven, 1964, no. 72.

Janos Scholz

Ottavio Leoni

Rome about 1578–Rome 1630

26 *Portrait of a Boy: Pietro Altemps*

Black and white chalk on blue paper. 9⅛ × 6⅛ inches (23.1 × 15.5 cm.). Lined.

Inscribed in pen and brown ink at lower left, *8 i/sitinbre*; at center, *1617*; in pencil at lower left corner, *D. Pietro Altemps* (this appears to be a transcription of an older inscription that shows through from the verso); numbered on mount in pen and black ink at lower left corner, *363*; on verso of mount various numbers and notations of attribution.

The pensive young boy so sympathetically portrayed here was a member of the prominent Altemps family, whose patronage of Leoni helped create the vogue for his portrait drawings among members of Roman society. Another portrait in the Morgan Library, less well-preserved than this fresh sheet, is identified as "G. Agnolo duca Altemps," and the resemblance suggests that he may have been Pietro's father or older brother.

There is no indication whether or not this sheet once might have been part of the collection of around four hundred of Leoni's drawings formed by Prince Borghese and seen by Mariette in Paris when it was sold in 1747 after the death of the last owner, M. d'Aubigny. The drawing was already mounted in its present form, with the inscribed number *363*, when it was in the possession of Sir Thomas Lawrence, as is proved by the fact that the impress of the dry stamp carries through to the verso of the old mount.

27 *Portrait of Settimia Manenti of Salerno*

Black, red, and white chalk on blue paper. 9⁵⁄₁₆ × 6⁵⁄₁₆ inches (23.6 × 16.1 cm.). Watermark: eagle in a circle, surmounted by a crown (close to Heawood 1256).

Inscribed in pen and brown ink at lower left, *434/sitinbre*; dated at lower center, *1629*; inscribed on verso in pen and brown ink, *Settimia Manenti Salernitana*; in pen and blue ink at lower margin, *coll. Verstolk*; in pencil, *Padovan*; various numbers.

Leoni's drawings almost invariably bear notations of the year and month of execution, but apparently not of the day. The significance of serial numbers like the *434* seen here is not yet known, but they were probably part of the artist's system for keeping track of the enormous number of portraits he drew and, in some instances, also engraved. It is usually stated that these inscriptions were made by the artist himself; the date 1637 on another female portrait in the Morgan Library (No. I, 25j), seemingly written by the same hand, perhaps was the result of a slip of the pen, since Leoni died in 1630. This portrait of Settimia Manenti of Salerno is a very late work, but confrontation with the earlier drawing in the exhibition (No. 26) reveals little change in the artist's basic formula.

PROVENANCE: Verstolk (according to inscription on verso, see Lugt 2490); William Mayor (Lugt 2799); Charles Fairfax Murray; purchased by J. Pierpont Morgan in London, 1910.

The Pierpont Morgan Library
No. I, 25i

Domenico Zampieri, called Domenichino

Bologna 1581–Naples 1641

28 *Landscape*

Pen and brown ink. 15⁵⁄₁₆ × 10³⁄₁₆ inches (38.5 × 25.9 cm.). Creases and repaired losses; foxed. Watermark: crown surmounted by a star (close to Heawood 1120).

Inscribed in pen and brown ink at lower left, *A. Carraci*; at lower right, *A. Carraci*.

Verso: Two slight red chalk sketches.

As indicated by the attribution a former owner inscribed at the lower right, the tradition of the Carracci is clearly felt in this ideal landscape composition with two pastoral figures. The draughtsmanship, however, is plainly Domenichino's. The figures seem to be more than mere *staffage*—the bearded older man obviously admonishes or directs the seated youth—but their significance is elusive. Although it is difficult to date Domenichino's landscapes, the Baer drawing is perhaps an earlier example than the following drawing No. 29. Since, according to John Pope-Hennessy, five-sixths of Domenichino's drawings are preserved at Windsor Castle, they are relatively rare elsewhere.

PROVENANCE: As incribed on verso, *Jan Enaht* (?) *1829* (1809?); Kaye Dowland (Lugt 691).

EXHIBITIONS: New York University, Institute of Fine Arts, "Master Drawings, XVI–XX Century, from the Collection of Curtis O. Baer," 1962, no. 6.

Curtis O. Baer

29 *Fortifications Seen across a River*

Pen and brown ink. 13⅛ × 8¹¹⁄₁₆ inches (33.3 × 22.1 cm.). Stains; repaired loss at lower margin. Indecipherable watermark.

Inscribed in pen and black ink at lower right, *Dominichino 35*; on verso, *Domenico Zampieri della dua prova*.

Verso: Landscape with an aqueduct, pen and brown ink.

It is possible that this view of fortified buildings on a river—and more especially the view of an aqueduct with mountains in the distance, on the verso—may have been sketched from nature. In any case, the draughtsman has at one time or another observed such things as the reflections of buildings and trees in the water, the cleavage of the rocky cliff side, and the small masted boat moored at the edge of the woods. The drawing does not appear to be associated with a painting, although in a general way the configuration of the wooded cliff with a cluster of buildings and a river at its base suggests the composition of the *Flight into Egypt* in the Louvre (repr. Evelina Borea, *Domenichino*, Milan, 1965, pl. XVII; dated about 1616). The present drawing, particularly the verso, is stylistically akin to several drawings at Windsor that Pope-Hennessy provisionally assigns to 1630–1631 (*The Drawings of Domenichino*, London, 1948, nos. 1674, 1677, 1678, fig. 63, and pls. 65, 63).

Giovanni Francesco Grimaldi (see No. 80), who made free use of Domenichino's drawings, copied the recto of the Morgan sheet in a drawing now at Windsor (Kurz, *Bolognese Drawings at Windsor*, no. 298). Practically the only change Grimaldi made was to show the boatmen seated. Grimaldi probably knew the Morgan drawing when it was in the possession of Francesco Raspantino, Domenichino's pupil, to whom he bequeathed the contents of his studio. For other Grimaldi drawings after Domenichino landscape sketches, see nos. 288 and 289 of the Windsor Bolognese catalogue.

PROVENANCE: Charles Fairfax Murray; purchased by J. Pierpont Morgan in London, 1910.

EXHIBITIONS: New York, Morgan Library, Landscape Drawings, 1953, no. 14.

The Pierpont Morgan Library
No. IV, 166a

Bernardo Strozzi

Genoa 1581–Venice 1644

30 *Head of a Woman*

Black chalk, with traces of white, on gray paper. 8⅞ × 6¼ inches (22.6 × 15.8 cm.). Lightly foxed and stained. Lined.

The epitome of Strozzi's generic type, this head was appropriately associated by Dr. Mortari with that of the Virgin in the small *Annunciation* in Budapest, a painting of the Genoese artist's Venetian years (1630–1644). The connection is probably that of period and type rather than of direct preparatory study, as the head in the painting is veiled, and not only the gaze, but the pose as well, is oriented upward. The features, however, are strikingly similar. Among Strozzi's relatively few drawings (the largest group known today is the twenty or so in the Palazzo Rosso, Genoa), the Manning sheet presents analogies with two others,

each of a female head, in the Museum Boymans-van Beuningen at Rotterdam (nos. I.65 and I.66). One of the few Strozzi drawings unquestionably related to a painting is the Cleveland Museum's black and red chalk study for its painting identified as Minerva or Bellona.

PROVENANCE: William E. Suida.

BIBLIOGRAPHY: Luisa Mortari, "Su Bernardo Strozzi," *Bollettino d'Arte*, XLII, 1955, p. 323, repr.

EXHIBITIONS: Venice, Ca' Pesaro, "La Pittura del Seicento a Venezia," 1959, no. 43 (drawings section), repr.; Dayton, Genoese Masters, 1962–1963, no. 98, repr.; New York, Finch College, Genoese Painters, 1964–1965, no. 33; Detroit, Italy 1600–1700, 1965, no. 203, repr.

Robert and Bertina Suida Manning

Giovanni Lanfranco

Parma 1582–Rome 1647

31 *St. Sylvester and the Dragon*

Pen and brown ink, brown and gray-brown wash, over faint indications in black chalk. 13¹³⁄₁₆ × 10 inches (35.1 × 25.3 cm.). Large brown oil stain in upper right quadrant; repaired loss at right center; abrasions and several smaller oil stains. Lined.

Inscription indecipherable, except for the name *Carraci*, in pen and brown ink at lower left margin. Richardson numbers on verso of lining; inscribed in pen and brown ink at upper left, *1 W 10 15*; in center, *1746/7*.

In its style and execution, this drawing still retains overtones of Lanfranco's masters, the Carracci, and in former years it was ascribed to Annibale Carracci, as the old inscription on the drawing and that of Richardson on his mount attest. Wittkower rejected the Carracci attribution in 1949; later Philip Pouncey and Jacob Bean independently recognized Lanfranco's hand and suggested a connection with the painting of this rather rare subject in the Carmelite church of St. Sylvester (popularly known as S. Teresa) at Caprarola. The picture, which differs considerably in composition from this drawing, is datable 1623–1624 on the basis of documents (*Die Künstlerbiographien von Giovanni Battista Passeri*, ed. J. Hess, Leipzig and Vienna, 1934, p. 154, note 5; p. 216, note 4). According to the *Golden Legend* of Voragine, Pope Sylvester was summoned by the Emperor Constantine to destroy a dragon that had daily slain over three hundred men with its pestilent breath, following the Emperor's conversion to Christianity. Accompanied by two priests, Sylvester went into the dragon's pit and rendered it harmless by binding its jaws with a cord, which he sealed with the emblem of the cross. The statue falling or being pulled off its pedestal in the background of the drawing is an allusion to the conquest of idolatry through the conversion of the Emperor.

PROVENANCE: Jonathan Richardson Senior (Lugt 2984); Earl of Aylesford (Lugt 58); Charles Fairfax Murray; purchased by J. Pierpont Morgan in London, 1910.

BIBLIOGRAPHY: Fairfax Murray, IV, no. 159, repr. (as Annibale Carracci).

The Pierpont Morgan Library
No. IV, 159

32 Two Studies of a Head

Black chalk, heightened with white, on brownish paper. 10½ × 8¾ inches (26.6 × 22.2 cm.).

Inscribed in pen and brown ink at lower right, *C: Lanfranco, D. 6* (?); numbered at upper right, *48*.

Verso: Black chalk studies of hands.

A fine example of Lanfranco's nervous, abbreviated chalk style. Slight touches of white give great pictorial vivacity to the summary design in black chalk. It is difficult to date this drawing—though it would seem to be a late rather than an early work—and it cannot be definitely connected with a painted work. Lanfranco had at his disposition a whole vocabulary of such heads and figures that he used and re-used in his frescoes and pictures.

PROVENANCE: Giovanni Piancastelli (no mark, see Lugt S. 2078a); Mr. and Mrs. Edward Brandegee (Lugt S. 1860c).

BIBLIOGRAPHY: "Drawings of Seven Centuries," *Apollo*, LXX, September 1959, p. 56, fig. II.

EXHIBITIONS: Oakland, Scholz Exhibition, 1957, no. 84; New York, M. Knoedler, "Great Master Drawings of Seven Centuries. Benefit Exhibition for Columbia University," 1959, no. 32, pl. XXXV; Hamburg, Scholz Exhibition, 1963, no. 81.

Janos Scholz

33 Seated Apostles and Putti

Red chalk. 5⅛ × 9¹¹⁄₁₆ inches (13 × 24.6 cm.). Light brown stains at right. Lined.

Inscription on verso that shows through on recto, *d . . . Lanfranco*.

Lanfranco left Rome for Naples in 1631 and remained there, prodigiously active as a decorator, until 1646, the year before his death. One of his major Neapolitan commissions, undertaken after the decoration of the now destroyed cupola of the Gesù Nuovo, was the painting in fresco of the groin-vaulted nave of the church of the Certosa di S. Martino. In the circular spaces along the center of the vault Lanfranco painted Christ appearing in a glory of angels, and in the triangular vaulted spaces above the windows he inserted groups of apostles, prophets, sibyls, and putti. Walter Vitzthum has identified this drawing as a scheme for one of these triangular areas. The broad-based triangular composition takes into consideration the whole area to be painted, while the faint red chalk indications of a narrower triangle suggest the area of the steeply rising vault that would be visible to the viewer standing directly below. Not only are Lanfranco's cloud-seated figures in this drawing, as in the fresco, strikingly Correggesque, but the handling of the red chalk reveals as well Lanfranco's early Emilian training. Two drawings for a first overall scheme for the Certosa vault were identified by Hermann Voss in the Teyler Museum at Haarlem (repr. *Bollettino d'Arte*, XLVI, 1961, p. 112).

PROVENANCE: Purchased by the Metropolitan Museum in London, 1965.

The Metropolitan Museum of Art
Rogers Fund, 65.66.6

34 The Martyrdom of the Apostle Matthias

Pen and brown ink, brown wash. Spots of red wash at upper right and left. 6⅞ × 6⅛ inches (17.5 × 15.6 cm.).

Another of Lanfranco's major Neapolitan commissions was the decoration of the interior of the church of the SS. Apostoli. He painted the vaults of the apse and nave with scenes of the martyrdoms of apostles and over the entrance door a vast fresco representing the Pool at Bethesda, a composition in an architectural setting that set a fashion in Neapolitan church decoration. Above this fresco, in triangular spaces to the left and right of a window, he painted further martyrdoms of apostles. This drawing, as the curved framing line at the right suggests, is for the *Martyrdom of St. Matthias*, represented to the right of the window. A great many of Lanfranco's preparatory drawings for SS. Apostoli have survived, and further studies for this same scene are at the Museo di Capodimonte in Naples (see Naples, Museo di Capodimonte, "Disegni di Lanfranco per la Chiesa dei Santi Apostoli," 1964, nos. 63–68), at Windsor (Blunt and Cooke, *Roman Drawings at Windsor*, nos. 194–195), in the Uffizi (repr. *Bollettino d'Arte*, XLVI, 1961, p. 114), and in the Metropolitan Museum (87.12.64, study of a running figure that appears in the first Windsor sketch). The present drawing is an excellent example of Lanfranco's Neapolitan pen manner, small in scale and remarkably succinct in the way that movement is suggested.

PROVENANCE: Walter Lowry, New York.

BIBLIOGRAPHY: Walter Vitzthum, "Seicento Drawings at the Cabinet des Dessins," *Burlington Magazine*, CII, 1960, p. 75, fig. 31; Jacob Bean and Walter Vitzthum, "Disegni del Lanfranco e del Benaschi," *Bollettino d'Arte*, XLVI, 1961, p. 110, fig. 16.

EXHIBITIONS: Detroit, Italy 1600–1700, 1965, no. 96, repr.

The Metropolitan Museum of Art
Gift of Walter Lowry, 56.219.4

Giovanni Battista Discepoli

Castagnola 1590–Milan 1660

35 *Joseph Sold by His Brethren*

Brush and red wash, heightened with white, over red chalk, on brown-washed paper. 11⅛ × 17⁹⁄₁₀ inches (28.2 × 43.7 cm.). Small repairs at lower margin.

Inscribed in pen and brown ink at lower left, *G. b. discepoli f.*; numbered in pen and black ink at upper left corner, *3.*; inscribed on verso, *Battᵃ Disepoli detto ... [Zop]po di Lugano*.

The style of this drawing, where the long-limbed, rather small-headed figures in the lively narrative scene are clad in graceful billowing draperies, as well as the extensive use of colored wash and white highlights, indicates a Lombard origin and reveals the predominant influence of Camillo Procaccini and of Morazzone. However, without the old attribution to Discepoli, called il Zoppo (the limper) of Lugano, inscribed on the sheet, one might be hard put to assign this spirited drawing to a specific Lombard artist. Padre Orlandi in his *Abecedario pittorico* tells us that Discepoli, now an almost forgotten artist, "adhered to the Procaccinesque manner and transformed it into a personal style that was most pleasing in its grace and the excellence of its color," a description that neatly characterizes this hitherto unpublished drawing. Few examples of Discepoli's draughtsmanship have survived; those attributed to him in the Ambrosiana (see Emma Spina Barelli, *Disegni di maestri lombardi del primo seicento*, Milan, 1959, nos. 84–87) are slight, while the present drawing shows him to be a vigorous if somewhat *retardataire* practitioner of a mannerist tradition that in Lombardy was prolonged well into the seventeenth century.

PROVENANCE: Giuseppe Vallardi (Lugt 1223); James Jackson Jarves, Florence; Cornelius Vanderbilt, New York.

The Metropolitan Museum of Art
Gift of Cornelius Vanderbilt, 80.3.333

Giovanni Francesco Barbieri, called Guercino

Cento 1591–Bologna 1666

36 *The Virgin Giving the Scapular to St. Albert*

Pen and brown ink, brown and gray-brown wash, over preliminary indications in black chalk, squared in black chalk. 15¾ × 10½ inches (40.1 × 26.7 cm.). Some foxing.

Inscribed in pen and black ink in an old hand at lower right, *Guerchin 1100*; numbered on verso in black chalk, *416*; ruled margin lines in red chalk.

This early drawing is a preparatory study for the painting in the Pinacoteca Civica at Cento, identified as the Virgin and Child with St. Simon Stock (Nefta Grimaldi, *Il Guercino*, Bologna [1957], pl. 89) and also as the Virgin and Child with St. Albert.

The latter identification is based on the engraving by Guercino's fellow townsman Giovanni Battista Pasqualini (Le Blanc, III, p. 145, no. 10), who frequently engraved after his paintings; the print is inscribed *Beatissima Vergine del Carmine et S. Alberto | in Cento Sup Permiss 1623. . . .* Executed in the reverse of the painting, it shows only its central motif of the Virgin bestowing on the saint the devotional scapular of two small squares joined with a cord—as opposed to the large cloth depicted in the Morgan drawing. St. Simon Stock and St. Albert are both Carmelite saints, and while the former is very frequently represented receiving the scapular, the identification of the contemporary print is not to be disregarded.

Although the squaring of the Morgan drawing indicates that the artist at one point regarded the composition as relatively fixed, only the central figure of the saint remains unaltered in the painting. The Child is shifted to the Virgin's left arm so that she can present the scapular with the right, the small angels disappear, and the dramatic gesture of the kneeling monk on the far right is relinquished, but reluctantly, as demonstrated by another drawing at Chatsworth (no. 519. Pen and wash, 41.5 × 26.9 cm.; executed in the opposite direction), which shows the monk still pointing but much less conspicuously. Typically, Fairfax Murray knew of the existence of the Chatsworth sheet, as he noted on the mat of the Morgan drawing. At the time the latter was "purchased after the sale [Hawley, 1891] from Daly," he quite properly described it in his records as "a drawing of the highest quality."

Mahon's suggested date of about 1614 for the painting is supported by the analogies that the Virgin and Child of this sheet present with the early drawings he discussed and illustrated in his article in the *Burlington Magazine*, LXX, 1937, pp. 184–185. In the painting Guercino added at the left a scene showing the rescue of souls from purgatory, a reference to the special favor the Virgin accorded the Carmelites, whom she delivered from purgatory, where they were easily recognizable by reason of their scapulars.

PROVENANCE: Sir Peter Lely (Lugt 2092); Jonathan Richardson Senior (Lugt 2184); Sir Joseph Hawley (according to the Fairfax Murray Notebooks); [Sir Henry Hawley] sale, London, Christie's, July 16, 1891, part of no. 218; Charles Fairfax Murray; purchased by J. Pierpont Morgan in London, 1910.

The Pierpont Morgan Library
No. IV, 168a

37 *Youth Kneeling before a Prelate*

Pen and brown ink, brown wash. 9⅚₆ × 7½ inches (23.7 × 19.1 cm.).

Verso: Another study of a youth kneeling before a prelate, in pen and brown ink, brown wash, partially showing through onto recto.

A dashing free sketch of the principal figures in an altarpiece representing St. William, duke of Aquitaine, receiving the monastic habit, painted in 1620 for the church of S. Gregorio in Bologna and now in the Pinacoteca of the same city (repr. Ellis Waterhouse, *Italian Baroque Painting*, London, 1962, fig. 96). Guercino's preparations for this large picture, justly celebrated as one of his most sumptuous early works, are recorded in a number of composition sketches. In the picture St. William, kneeling before St. Benedict of Aniane who is seated at the left, pulls a monastic cowl over his head; a drawing at Windsor (Inv. 2475) gives this solution. In three drawings at the Louvre (Inv. 6884, 6885, 6886) St. William, kneeling or standing before the prelate, already wears the habit. On both the recto and verso of the Metropolitan sheet the kneeling saint, still clad in armor, holds a cross in his hand, and this scheme is elaborated in reverse with the addition of other figures in a further Louvre drawing (Inv. 6883; repr. Gabriel Rouchès, *Musée du Louvre. Dessins italiens du XVIIe siècle*, Paris, n.d., no. 14); and in a hitherto unnoticed double-sided sheet at Berlin-Dahlem (Kupferstichkabinett, 16362, mistakenly attributed to Agostino Carracci) St. William, clad in armor, stands before the bishop. A complete composition study with notable variations was in the collection of Baron Vivant Denon (repr. *Monuments*, III, pl. 209).

PROVENANCE: William Russell (Lugt 2648); purchased by the Metropolitan Museum in London, 1908.

BIBLIOGRAPHY: Roger Fry, "Recent Acquisitions of Drawings," *Metropolitan Museum of Art Bulletin*, January 1909, p. 7; Bean, *100 European Drawings*, no. 30, repr.

The Metropolitan Museum of Art
Rogers Fund, 08.227.29

38 Satire on Gambling

Pen and brown ink, brown wash. 10⅛ × 15½ inches (25.7 × 39.4 cm.). Slight staining; three very small losses at lower right corner. Lined.

Inscribed by the artist in pen and brown ink at upper left, *Sicut mat*; on a block at the left, *DAI DAI/AL' MAT./ LE' AMATIÌ P̲ CHÈ LA'/MANGIA DEL CERVEL/ D' GAT' AL LOV* (Indeed mad. Give give to the mad one. He went mad because he eats cat brain[s] with egg[s]).

No one has yet come forth with a better description of the curious subject of this remarkable drawing than Fairfax Murray, who supplied the present title. The drawing would appear to be highly personal in its reference, since the central figure, who is literally losing not only his shirt but his shoes, hose, and other belongings as well, is a man with crossed eyes, and the artist's nickname "Il Guercino" (The Squinter) derived from his pronounced strabismus, which is as obvious in the *Self-Portrait* in the Louvre and in Ottavio Leoni's engraved portrait of 1623 as it is here. On the victim's strange feathered headdress (feathers, it will be recalled, are a symbol of folly), one can plainly distinguish tarot playing cards in the suits of coins and swords, and possibly also staves and cups. A similar but not identical headdress, which is only half feathered, is worn by a figure, probably a fool judging from his costume, in Guercino's drawing of a theater scene in the British Museum (repr. *British Museum Quarterly*, XII, 1937–1938, pl. 10). The owl pursued by sharp-beaked birds seems to be a secondary allusion to the main theme. The scene appears to take place on a platform in an open square, as if the victim were on public display with only the woman as an ally. The inscription, which must hold the key to the meaning of the subject, perhaps goes back to a proverb or local folklore.

There is no documentary evidence for dating this drawing. On a stylistic basis, it would seem to belong to the years before Guercino's trip to Rome in 1621.

PROVENANCE: Sir Joshua Reynolds (Lugt 2364); Lord Palmerston (according to Fairfax Murray); Charles Fairfax Murray; purchased by J. Pierpont Morgan in London, 1910.

BIBLIOGRAPHY: Fairfax Murray, I, no. 101, repr.; Mildred Akin Lynes, "The Drawings of Guercino in the Dan Fellows Platt Collection, Englewood, New Jersey," unpublished thesis, New York University, Institute of Fine Arts, 1940, p. 49; Parker, *Ashmolean Catalogue*, II, p. 448, under no. 870.

The Pierpont Morgan Library
No. I, 101

39 The Visitation

Pen and brown ink, brown wash. 9¾ × 7½ inches (24.8 × 19.1 cm.). Repaired loss of upper right corner.

Under the date of June 7, 1632, Guercino's account book records full payment for a *Visitation* and a *Martyrdom of St. John and St. Paul* executed for the Cathedral at Reggio Emilia (Calvi, *Notizie*, p. 66, and Malvasia, II, pp. 262, 310). Denis Mahon has related three drawings in the Morgan Library to this dual commission: two composition studies for the *Visitation*, now in the museum at Rouen, and a double-sided sheet of studies for the *Martyrdom of St. John and St. Paul* (see No. 40 below), now at Toulouse in the Musée des Augustins (paintings repr. Nefta Grimaldi, *Il Guercino*, Bologna [1957], pls. 97, 98). The solution proposed in the present sheet was rejected by the artist in favor of a composition where details of the setting like the balustrade and balcony were eliminated and the active movements of the figures abandoned for poses of quiet monumentality. The Library's other Visitation scene, a smaller drawing that is somewhat rougher in its execution, is much closer to the painting (1956.21. Pen and brown ink, brown wash, 22.3 × 16.6 cm., formerly Johann Török collection). An entirely different conception of the theme, showing Elizabeth assisting Mary in dismounting from the donkey on which she had traveled, is in the Art Museum, Princeton University (see Bibliography).

PROVENANCE: Sir Charles Greville (Lugt 549); Earls of Warwick (Lugt 2600); Charles Fairfax Murray; purchased by J. Pierpont Morgan in London, 1910.

BIBLIOGRAPHY: J. Bean, *Italian Drawings in the Art Museum, Princeton University*, Princeton, 1966, under no. 39.

The Pierpont Morgan Library
No. I, 101f

40 *The Martyrdom of St. John and St. Paul* Verso: *The Martyrdom of St. John and St. Paul*

Pen and brown ink, brown wash. 9⅞ × 11⅞ inches (25.1 × 30.1 cm.). Slight foxing.

Both recto and verso of this sheet embody preliminary ideas for the painting of the subject, now preserved in the Musée des Augustins, Toulouse, but originally one of the two pictures executed for the Cathedral at Reggio Emilia in 1632 (see No. 39 above). The painting is vertical in format, with a representation of the Virgin and Child in the clouds above the scene of the martyrdom of the brothers John and Paul, who were presumably decapitated in 363 under Julian the Apostate for refusing to worship pagan gods. (Five years earlier, in 1627, Guercino had supplied Reggio Emilia with a painting of another decapitation scene, the *Martyrdom of S. Giacomo*, now lost. Preparatory drawings for this project, which afford an instructive comparison with the studies for the later Toulouse painting, are noted under no. 71 of the catalogue of the exhibition "Disegni del seicento emiliano," at the Brera, Milan, 1959).

The variant groupings of the executioner and his victims that Guercino's facile pen brilliantly laid out on both sides of the sheet were only experimental stages in the evolution of the final composition. This was more nearly anticipated in the double-sided sheet in the Witt Collection (*Hand-List*, no. 1341). Guercino sometimes studied the clothed figures of his paintings in the nude, or nearly so, as is here true of the swordsman. Of the three positions of the swordsman's arm that he toyed with on the verso of the Morgan drawing, he finally selected the lowest and swung the figure completely around so that in the painting it is seen from the back. He retained the location of the corpse on the right of the scene, but chose to show it chest down as on the recto of this sheet. Denis

Mahon reports that there are a number of other studies for the Toulouse painting, one of which he himself owns (formerly Oppenheimer collection, sale, London, Christie's, July 10–14, 1936, no. 102).

PROVENANCE: Sir Charles Greville (Lugt 549); Earls of Warwick (Lugt 2600); unidentified collector's mark in pen and black ink at lower right, *J* (probably Lugt 1404); Charles Fairfax Murray; purchased by J. Pierpont Morgan in London, 1910.

The Pierpont Morgan Library
No. I, 101h

41 *The Martyrdom of St. Bartholomew*

Pen and brown ink, brown wash. 9¾ × 7½ inches (24.8 × 19.1 cm.). Very small repaired tear and losses at corners and lower margin.

The receipt of earnest money for a *Martyrdom of St. Bartholomew*, "nella quale anderanno sei figure" for an agreed price of 600 *ducatoni*, is recorded in Guercino's account book under January 16, 1635; a payment on account is mentioned on September 1, 1636; final payment, on December 4, 1636; and a bonus that included some lengths of fine Sienese cloth, on April 8, 1637 (Calvi, *Notizie*, pp. 73–74, 78, 79, 80; Malvasia, II, pp. 263, 313, 315, 316). The painting still hangs in the church of S. Martino at Siena for which it was commissioned, but because of its damaged state the composition is better studied in a contemporary copy now in the church of S. Barnaba at Marino near Rome, painted for Cardinal Colonna, archbishop of Bologna, by Giacinto Campana and retouched, according to Malvasia, by Guercino himself. (The price of 600 *ducatoni* for six figures is an indication that Guercino, who based his charges on the number of full-length figures, half-lengths, etc., was receiving one hundred *ducatoni* per figure at this period.)

In addition to the Morgan drawing, Denis Mahon has connected drawings in the Princeton University Art Museum (Platt Bequest, 48.734) and the Art Institute of Chicago (60.832) with the S. Martino commission though none offers the solution finally adopted in the painting. The Morgan and Princeton compositions both include the six figures specified in the account book entry of January 16, 1635 (it could possibly be argued that there are more than six in the Princeton drawing); the Chicago sheet shows only the saint, in three-quarter length, and a single soldier. The *Hand-List* of the Witt Collection lists as no. 1337 *The Flaying of St. Bartholomew*, from the collection of the Earl of Gainsborough, and another drawing of the subject, formerly in the collection of H. S. Reitlinger (sale, London, Sotheby's, December 9, 1953, no. 53), is owned by Stephen Korda, London. The account book mentions another painting of St. Bartholomew under dates of August 3, 1660, and March 7, 1661 (Calvi, *Notizie*, pp. 152–153).

PROVENANCE: Earls of Warwick (Lugt 2600); Charles Fairfax Murray; purchased by J. Pierpont Morgan in London, 1910.

BIBLIOGRAPHY: J. Bean, *Italian Drawings in The Art Museum, Princeton University*, Princeton, 1966, under no. 40.

The Pierpont Morgan Library
No. I, 101e

42 *The Virgin of the Rosary*

Pen and brown ink, brown wash. 14 1/16 × 10 3/8 inches (35.8 × 26.4 cm.). Small repaired losses at margins; irregular crease at upper center. Watermark: coat of arms (six fleurs-de-lis in a shield, surmounted by a crown).

Inscribed on verso in pencil, pen and brown ink with various numbers; in red chalk, *1141*.

Charles Rogers included W. W. Ryland's engraved facsimile of this drawing (1763) in his *Collection of Prints in Imitation of Drawings*, 1778, remarking, "Guercino painted this Subject twice; once in 1637 for his Highness of Savoy, which picture cost 600 Ducatones; and again in 1643 by the direction of Cardinal Araceli Bishop of Osimo, for an Altar-piece in the Church of St. Dominic in that city (*Felsina pittrice*, II, pp. 371, 373). In this Drawing, which was probably made for one of those pictures, he has very poetically treated its Subject." Unfortunately, little can be added to Rogers's statement except to note that the Osimo altarpiece was first commissioned in 1641 (Calvi, *Notizie*, pp. 98, 104; for references to 1637 painting, see pp. 80, 83–84). Both paintings are described in the account book as showing the Madonna and Child with St. Dominic and St. Catherine of Siena,

and angels. From the point of view of style, the Morgan drawing's affinities with the *St. Francis* of 1645 and the *St. Michael* of 1644 (repr. Denis Mahon, *Studies in Seicento Art and Theory*, London, 1947, figs. 3 and 16) would seem to suggest a link with the later Osimo painting.

Other representations of this popular devotional subject are to be found in chalk drawings in the British Museum (1910.2.12.8) and at Chatsworth. Thomas S. Wragg writes that the Chatsworth drawing carries a notation by A. E. Popham associating it with the 1637 picture.

PROVENANCE: Michael Rysbrack (engraved 1763, by W. W. Ryland when in Rysbrack's collection); Sir Thomas Lawrence (Lugt 2445); Charles Fairfax Murray; purchased by J. Pierpont Morgan in London, 1910.

BIBLIOGRAPHY: Charles Rogers, *A Collection of Prints in Imitation of Drawings*, II, London, 1778, pp. 108–111, repr. in facsimile; Fairfax Murray, IV, no. 167, repr.

The Pierpont Morgan Library
No. IV, 167

43 *St. Philip Neri*

Pen and brown ink, brown wash. 5 11/16 × 9 5/16 inches (14.5 × 23.7 cm.). Light foxing.

Guercino's account book indicates that during the 1640s and 1650s he painted the subject of St. Philip Neri (1515–1595) a number of times. The painting, commissioned on January 26, 1646, and paid for in full on November 14, 1647, is still preserved in the church of S. Maria di Galliera in Bologna for which it was made (Calvi, *Notizie*, pp. 112, 117; painting repr. Nefta Grimaldi, *Il Guercino*, Bologna [1957], pl. 120). This and No. 44 of the exhibition show two of the solutions considered in planning the lower half of the painting, a vertical composition that represents the saint, his upraised arms supported by two angels, at the moment of his vision of the Virgin and Child. It is hard to say which drawing preceded the other, but possibly the more schematic although more highly keyed Cremer sheet was first. The ecstatic note diminishes perceptibly in No. 44 and in the painting, a progression between preliminary ideas and final version that is characteristic of the later Guercino, as was fully analyzed by Denis Mahon in *Studies in Seicento Art and Theory*, London, 1947. In No. 44 the angels are increasingly prominent and moving to the fore as in the picture, and details like the saint's head and the fluttering ribbon of the left angel's drapery are defined more specifically. Conceivably, the upraised arm and hand of the right angel in the Scholz study may even have inspired the lifting of the saint's arms to this point in the painting, although this upward movement of the arm is already begun in the *pentimento* of the saint's arm in the right group of the Cremer sheet.

BIBLIOGRAPHY: Walter Vitzthum, "Drawings from the Scholz Collection in Germany," *Master Drawings*, I, no. 4, 1963, pp. 58–59, pl. 41.

J. Theodor Cremer

44 *St. Philip Neri*

Pen and brown ink, brown wash. 9 ¹⁵⁄₁₆ × 11 ⁷⁄₁₆ inches (25.2 × 29 cm.). Repaired losses in lower half; small losses at right margin; diagonal crease across upper right corner; various creases; very light foxing.

Numbered in pencil at upper right, *70*.

A study, as Denis Mahon was the first to point out, for an altarpiece in S. Maria di Galliera, Bologna. See No. 43 above.

PROVENANCE: Benno Geiger, Venice.

BIBLIOGRAPHY: Walter Vitzthum, "Drawings from the Scholz Collection in Germany," *Master Drawings*, I, no. 4, 1963, pp. 58–59, pl. 40; "Italian Drawings from the Collection of Janos Scholz," *Metropolitan Museum of Art Bulletin*, May 1965, Part II, pp. 337, 340, repr. cover.

EXHIBITIONS: Scholz Exhibitions: Oakland, 1957, no. 78, repr.; Hagerstown, 1960–1961, no. 39; Columbia, S.C., 1961, no. 46; Hamburg, 1963, no. 78, pl. 34; New Haven, 1964, no. 64, pl. 12.

Janos Scholz

45 *Silvio Discovering the Wounded Dorinda, Supported by Linco*

Pen and brown ink, brown wash. 11 ⅜ × 10 ¹³⁄₁₆ inches (28.9 × 27.5 cm.). Foxed. Lined.

During the time that Guercino was at work on the *St. Philip Neri* for S. Maria di Galliera, Bologna, he received a commission from Count Alfonso of Novellara for a representation of Silvio and Dorinda, two of the characters of *Il Pastor Fido*, the poet Giovanni Battista Guarini's pastoral drama, first published in 1590 and first publicly performed in Turin in 1595. The artist's account book shows the first payment on account for the painting was received on January 16, 1647, and final payment on July 23 of the same year (Calvi, *Notizie*, pp. 115–116), which was the most profitable of his career (4,168 *scudi*). As might be expected, the present sheet and No. 44 are identical in style and handling, each being a singularly fine example of Guercino's draughtsmanship of the period. As in the case of the two studies for *St. Philip Neri*, the present composition does not embody the final concept settled upon in the painting, now at Dresden. Here again there is the tendency to open up the composition in the interest of a more classic symmetry and clarity of contour, achieved in the painting mainly by showing Dorinda posed quite differently on Linco's left and Silvio kneeling on one knee. The incident represented is the hunter Silvio's discovery that he has unwittingly wounded Dorinda, whom in her disguise he had mistaken for a wolf. Her rescuer is Linco, the faithful shepherd who gives the play its name.

PROVENANCE: Charles Fairfax Murray; purchased by J. Pierpont Morgan in London, 1910.

*The Pierpont Morgan Library
No. I, 101g*

46 *Standing Boy Holding a Bowl*

Red chalk. 10 ⁷⁄₁₆ × 7 ⁷⁄₁₆ inches (26.5 × 18.9 cm.). Paste stains at margins. Lined.

This red chalk drawing of a boy in scant classical drapery holding a bowl to his lips may be a study for a figure of Ganymede, cupbearer of the gods. Neither a Ganymede nor this particular youthful figure is to be found in any of Guercino's surviving pictures, but the style of this sensitive drawing, where subtle contrasts of light and shade so successfully indicate the modeling of back and head, suggests that it dates from the artist's middle period. In any case, the red chalk is used more freely than in the smoothly finished figure drawings produced in such abundance by Guercino in his later years.

PROVENANCE: Edward Bouverie (Lugt 325); John, Lord Northwick; Northwick sale, London, Sotheby's, November 1–4, 1920, no. 14; sale, London, Sotheby's, March 12, 1963, no. 34, repr., bought by the Metropolitan Museum.

BIBLIOGRAPHY: Bean, *100 European Drawings*, no. 31, repr.

The Metropolitan Museum of Art
Rogers Fund, 63.75.2

47 *Virgin and Child with a Book and a Pot of Pinks*

Red chalk, stumped in some areas. $10\frac{1}{8} \times 7\frac{1}{2}$ inches (25.7 × 19 cm.). Very slight foxing. Lined.

Francesco Curti (1603–1670), a Bolognese print-maker, engraved this ingratiating drawing, which was very possibly executed with that precise purpose in mind. Guercino was resident in Bologna from 1642 until his death in 1666, and both drawing and print (Le Blanc, II, p. 77, no. 2) were perhaps made near the beginning of this period, if not earlier. Curti's engraving, which is in the reverse of the drawing, was dedicated to Giovanni Battista Ferri, a Bolognese patron of Guercino who is recorded in the artist's account book as paying for a half-length *St. Jerome* and other works in the years 1637–1638 (Calvi, *Notizie*, pp. 83, 85).

For an early treatment of a somewhat similar subject, in which it is the Child who plucks the flower, see the red chalk drawing in the Accademia, Venice (*Burlington Magazine*, LXX, 1937, p. 184, fig. 1; also Matteo Marangoni, *Guercino*, Milan [1959], pl. 47).

PROVENANCE: William Mayor (Lugt 2799); Charles Fairfax Murray; purchased by J. Pierpont Morgan in London, 1910.

BIBLIOGRAPHY: James Watrous, *The Craft of Old-Master Drawings*, Madison, 1957, pp. 96, 151.

The Pierpont Morgan Library
No. IV, 168g

48 *The Holy Family*

Colored chalks (black, red, blue, brown, ochre), blue-gray wash. $14\frac{1}{16} \times 10\frac{9}{16}$ inches (35.8 × 26.8 cm.). Lined.

Inscribed in pen and brown ink at upper left, *ZAMC*.

The introduction of color is most unusual in Guercino's *oeuvre*. There are, for example, no comparable instances among the great hoard of the artist's drawings at Windsor, but the color here is harmonious and so entirely homogenous with the rest of the drawing that it must be concluded, as Denis Mahon suggested, that this is an instance of a presentation sheet made for a special patron or friend. It recalls that Guercino practiced drawing as an independent art, but seldom so elaborately as here.

When the drawing was in the possession of the Venetian collector and *amateur* A. M. Zanetti, it was engraved, in reverse, by Francesco Bartolozzi. (Fairfax Murray's note in the first volume of his publication of the Morgan drawings, which cites the engraving of the drawing when it was "in Algarotti's collection" was most likely the result of a trick of memory that substituted the name of one famous eighteenth-century Venetian *amateur* for the other.) The Baron Vivant Denon, another distinguished owner of this sheet, had a great series of Guercino drawings, many of which like the present one were engraved by Bartolozzi and came from the collection of Count Zanetti, but the *Holy Family* is not among the drawings reproduced in the baron's *Monuments*.

Mariette mentions the Morgan drawing in a note, dated 1768, in his extra-illustrated copy of *Nuova Raccolta di alcuni disegni del Barbieri da Cento, detto el Guercino*, Rome, 1764 (see bibliography below). Discussing Bartolozzi's prints after Guercino's drawings, he remarks that one of the drawings Bartolozzi reproduced had been bought from Guercino's heirs by a "M. Jenings" who had had it sent to England. He then notes, "Un autre de ces desseins, où l'enfant Jésus est représenté têtant sa mère, est dans le cabinet de Zanetti. Il est legerement colorié et le même M. Jenings m'en a fait un grand éloge." It is surely the "lightly colored" Morgan sheet that Mr. Jenings praised so highly to Mariette. (Apropos of the 1768 date of Mariette's note and Mr. Jenings's purchase from "les héritiers du Guerchin," see Consul Smith's letter of April 9, 1768, concerning the Gennari collection, in Francis Haskell, *Patrons and Painters*, London, 1963, pp. 392–393.)

It should be added that in the 1826 sale catalogue

of Vivant Denon's collection, under Cesare Gennari, no. 441, it is stated: "Dessin capital aux crayons rouge et noir, avec un peu de pastel et d'aquarelle sur papier blanc. Il représente la Vierge près de Saint Joseph, présentant le sein au petit Jésus. On ne peut pousser plus loin le charme de l'effet que dans ce dessin." One wonders what prompted A. N. Pérignon, who prepared the paintings and drawings section of the catalogue, to go against the earlier evidence and attribute the drawing to Guercino's nephew, Cesare Gennari (1641–1688). If he was correct, our assessment of Cesare's ability as a draughtsman must be revised.

PROVENANCE: Antonio Maria Zanetti; Baron Dominique Vivant Denon (Lugt 779); Robert S. Holford (Lugt 2243); Charles Fairfax Murray; purchased by J. Pierpont Morgan in London, 1910.

BIBLIOGRAPHY: Mariette, *Abécédario*, I, p. 63; Fairfax Murray, I, no. 99, repr.

EXHIBITIONS: Hartford, Wadsworth Atheneum, "The Pierpont Morgan Treasures," 1960, no. 74.

The Pierpont Morgan Library
No. I, 99

49 *Fireworks in a Piazza*

Pen and brown ink, gray-brown wash. 7⁵/₁₆ × 10⁷/₁₆ inches (18.5 × 26.5 cm.).

Guercino has observed a group of city folk standing in a piazza watching fireworks set off from a tower while another pyrotechnic display is being activated under the straw construction at the left. A similar conical construction commands the attention of an excited crowd in a drawing attributed to Guercino at Chatsworth (Courtauld photo 62/1049). Such scenes from popular life delighted Bolognese artists, and Guercino was a particular master at jotting them down impromptu in pen and wash. The present example probably dates from fairly early in his career.

PROVENANCE: Sir Charles Greville (Lugt 549); Earls of Warwick (Lugt 2600); J. P. Richter, London; purchased by the Metropolitan Museum in London, 1912.

BIBLIOGRAPHY: George S. Hellman, "Drawings by Italian Artists in the Metropolitan Museum of Art," *Print Collector's Quarterly*, VI, 1916, p. 180, repr. p. 181; Metropolitan Museum, *European Drawings*, I, repr. no. 29;

"Some Italian Drawings in the Metropolitan Museum," *Connoisseur*, CX, 1943, p. 151, repr. no. IX.

The Metropolitan Museum of Art
Rogers Fund, 12.56.12

50 *Landscape with a Volcano*

Brush, brown wash, on blue paper. 10³/₁₆ × 14⁵/₈ inches (25.8 × 37.2 cm.). Small loss at left margin, center.

A drawing done purely with the brush is unusual if not unique among Guercino's numerous landscapes, which are almost invariably drawn with the pen. Another lavishly washed drawing, but with some basic pen work, *Landscape with Shepherds Peering into a Chasm*, is to be found in the collection of John Nicholas Brown, Providence (repr. Russell, pl. XVIII). Guercino never fails to animate his landscape compositions with a few figures as he does here. Whether he himself was ever as near to a volcano as the figures he depicts is not known.

The border of the old mount of the present sheet, a patterning of parallel lines in red ink, may be a variant of the similar ornamented borders in black ink that are the hallmark of the collection of Guercino's nephews, Benedetto and Cesare Gennari and their descendants, and the drawing may therefore have descended through the long line of owners listed under Lugt S. 2858c.

PROVENANCE: Benedetto and Cesare Gennari (?); Lord Northwick (according to Russell); William Bateson (Lugt S. 2604a).

BIBLIOGRAPHY: Archibald G. B. Russell, *Drawings by Guercino*, London, 1923, pp. 22, 51, pl. 14; "Italian Drawings from the Collection of Janos Scholz," *Metropolitan Museum of Art Bulletin*, May 1965, Part II, p. 340, repr.

EXHIBITIONS: London, Burlington Fine Arts Club, 1923, no. 3; London, Magnasco Society, 1927; Scholz Exhibitions: Oakland, 1957, no. 75; Columbia, S.C., 1961, no. 44; Hamburg, 1963, no. 79, pl. 36; New Haven, 1964, no. 65.

Janos Scholz

51 *River Landscape with Swimmers*

Pen and brown ink. 10⁵/₁₆ × 16¹³/₁₆ inches (26.2 × 42.8 cm.). A few repaired tears; slight abrasion at lower left.

Although landscape played little part in Guercino's paintings, he was a prolific landscape draughtsman, and his production has been further magnified—and distorted—by the endless copies of his drawings of this kind. For example, on p. 64 of the Crozat sale catalogue of 1741 there are listed three lots of drawings, seventy-three in all, "dont quelques-uns de Païsages faits à la plume," by the artist's nephews, Cesare and Benedetto Gennari, and other of Guercino's pupils; and Mariette's sale catalogue of 1775 (p. 26, no. 153) included eight copies of Guercino landscapes he himself had drawn.

The drawing exhibited compares favorably with the authentic group of more elaborate landscapes at Chatsworth, which were engraved by Jean Pesne (1623–1700) and issued, without date, with a dedication by Guercino's nephews to Francesco II, Duke of Modena. Two of the Chatsworth series, which are about the same size as this drawing, are illustrated in the exhibition catalogue "Old Master Drawings from Chatsworth," circulated by the Smithsonian Institution, 1962–1963, figs 29, 30. There is also a bathing scene in the Chatsworth group.

Little is known about the chronology of Guercino's landscape drawings, but McComb was probably correct in placing this drawing later rather than earlier.

PROVENANCE: François Renaud (Lugt S. 1042); Moriz von Fries (Lugt 2903); A. C. Poggi (Lugt 617); Sir Charles Greville (Lugt 549); Earls of Warwick (Lugt 2600); Charles Fairfax Murray; purchased by J. Pierpont Morgan in London, 1910.

BIBLIOGRAPHY: Fairfax Murray, IV, no. 168, repr.; Arthur McComb, *The Baroque Painters of Italy*, Cambridge, Mass., 1934, p. 33, fig. 34; Mildred Akin Lynes, "The Drawings of Guercino in the Dan Fellows Platt Collection, Englewood, New Jersey," unpublished thesis, New York University, Institute of Fine Arts, 1940, p. 30; Agnes Mongan, review of "Italian Drawings 1330–1780: An Exhibition at the Smith College Museum of Art," *Art Bulletin*, XXIV, 1942, p. 93.

EXHIBITIONS: Northampton, Smith College Museum of Art, "Italian Drawings, 1330–1780," 1941, no. 32; New York, Morgan Library, Landscape Drawings, 1953, no. 15.

The Pierpont Morgan Library
No. IV, 168

Giovanni Mannozzi, called Giovanni da San Giovanni

S. Giovanni Valdarno 1592–Florence 1636

52 *St. Paul Led into Damascus*

Pen and brown ink, brown wash. $7 \times 15\frac{5}{8}$ inches (17.7×39.7 cm.). Sheet cut to the shape of a lunette; vertical crease at center.

Study for the lunette above the altar of the Cappella Inghirami in the Duomo at Volterra, as Philip Pouncey was the first to point out. The subject of the drawing has on other occasions been described as the Castigation of St. Paul or the Martyrdom of St. Paul, but it clearly represents the blinded Paul being led into Damascus, an incident suitable to the position of Giovanni da San Giovanni's lunette-shaped fresco above Domenichino's altarpiece representing the Martyrdom of St. Paul. The Inghirami chapel was built and lavishly decorated at the expense of Jacopo Inghirami of Volterra, admiral of the Tuscan fleet that had been victorious at the siege of Bône in 1607. Pictures for the side walls representing scenes from the life of St. Paul were commissioned from Matteo Rosselli and Francesco Curradi, both Florentines, while the altarpiece was ordered from Domenichino in Rome. Giovanni da San Giovanni was assigned the task of decorating the vault, divided into several sections by stucco ornament, with further incidents from the life of the apostle. His work must have been finished by 1622, when Neri Papucci wrote from Rome to the admiral's nephew announcing that Domenichino's nearly completed altarpiece for the chapel was a work of "maestria grandissima," but regretting that Domenichino's St. Paul did not look like the apostle as Giovanni da San Giovanni had painted him on the vault of the chapel (Odoardo H. Giglioli, *Giovanni da San Giovanni*, Florence, 1949, p. 41). Giovanni's lunette above the altar is a pleasantly animated narrative scene. Historically the event took place outside the gates of Damascus, but here the thirteenth-century Baptistry of Volterra appears above the city walls. In the fresco (repr. C. Ricci, *Volterra. L'Italia artistica, 18*, Bergamo, 1914, p. 128) the onlookers who appear in the right foreground of the drawing are given the features of various members of the Inghirami family, thus forming a group portrait that adds another anachronistic local note to the scene.

EXHIBITIONS: Scholz Exhibitions: Oakland, 1961, no. 75, repr.; Columbia, S.C., 1961, no. 72, repr.; Hamburg, 1963, no. 142, pl. 31; New Haven, 1964, no. 63.

Janos Scholz

Pietro Berrettini, called Pietro da Cortona

Cortona 1596–Rome 1669

53 *The Queen of Sheba Bringing Presents to Solomon*

Pen and brown ink, brown wash, heightened with blue and white, on brownish paper. $8\frac{5}{8} \times 14\frac{1}{8}$ inches (21.9×36 cm.).

Inscribed on verso in pen and light brown ink, *Pietro Cortone*; in pen and dark brown ink, *Pietro Berettini da Cortona. ob: 1669. ætat: 73. Abedario.* [sic] *fol: 356*; in another hand, *38 28.* Collector's mark of Janos Scholz at lower left (Lugt S. 2933b).

Preparatory study for one of the incidents in the story of Solomon painted by Cortona on the vault of the Gallery of the Palazzo Mattei in Rome. Another somewhat less elaborate study for the same scene is in the Teyler Museum at Haarlem (repr. Briganti, *Cortona*, fig. 14); the two sheets are among the earliest surviving drawings by Cortona.

The story of the young Cortona's collaboration in the decoration of the Palazzo Mattei is complex. The enlargement of the palace, undertaken by the architect Carlo Maderno on the commission of Marchese Asdrubale Mattei, got under way in 1598, and by the beginning of the second decade of the seventeenth century was sufficiently advanced for the decoration of the vaults of the rooms on the *piano nobile* to begin. Asdrubale Mattei employed a number of well-known painters for the task: Albani, Lanfranco, Domenichino, Antonio Carracci among them. The Gallery seems to have been one of the last rooms to be built, and it must have been about 1618 that Pietro Paolo Bonzi of Cortona, called Il Gobbo dei Carracci, a former pupil and assistant of Annibale Carracci, was commissioned to decorate the vault of the new room. Though the whole decorative scheme, involving narrative scenes treated as *quadri riportati* against a back-

ground of monochrome decoration crossed by garlands of fruit, flowers, and vegetables, is ascribed to Bonzi alone in most contemporary documents, the latter, a specialist in ornamental decoration, must have had assistance for the narrative sections of the scheme. Four of these scenes, the two rectangular sections representing the Queen of Sheba before Solomon and the Idolatry of Solomon, and two of the lateral hexagonal sections, those representing the Death of Joab and Solomon Giving Thanks, may on stylistic grounds be attributed with certainty to Pietro da Cortona. They are his earliest surviving works in the fresco technique that he was later to use with such imaginative brilliance. Jakob Hess (*Commentari*, V, 1954, pp. 300 ff.) and Briganti (*Cortona*, pp. 160–163; the frescoes repr. figs. 8 ff.) have discussed at length the respective roles of Cortona and Bonzi in the Mattei Gallery, and the passage in a manuscript text by Giulio Mancini that gives the unique contemporary testimony to Cortona's participation. Vitzthum has pointed out that Cortona borrowed the composition of *The Queen of Sheba before Solomon* from a late mannerist fresco in the Palazzo Giustiniani, but pulled the loose composition together to form a tight Polidoresque relief typical of his early style.

PROVENANCE: Johann Goll van Franckenstein (Lugt 2987, N 2369 of the collection).

BIBLIOGRAPHY: Briganti, *Cortona*, p. 309, fig. 13; Walter Vitzthum, "Pietro da Cortona" (review of Briganti's monograph), *Burlington Magazine*, CV, 1963, p. 215.

EXHIBITIONS: Scholz Exhibitions: Hagerstown, 1960–1961, no. 42; Hamburg, 1961, no. 42; Columbia, S.C., 1961, no. 28.

Janos Scholz

54 *Offering to Pomona*

Pen and brown ink, brown wash, over black chalk. $8\frac{7}{16} \times 11\frac{13}{16}$ inches (21.4×30 cm.). Lined.

Inscribed on mount in pen and brown ink at center, *Pietro da Cortona*; at lower left, *n⁰ 53*; on verso of lining in pen and brown ink at upper center, Richardson numbers; on verso in a later hand at center, *Triumph of Pomona/Peter De Cortona.*

Typical of the early style of Cortona, this vigorous pen drawing is a study, in reverse, for one of the now repainted frescoes of the Gallery on the second floor of the Villa Sacchetti at Castel Fusano near

Ostia. The villa, later Chigi property, was built and decorated between the years 1626 and 1630. Cortona was charged with the decoration of the villa, possibly also of its architectural design, by his patron the Marchese Marcello Sacchetti, whose portrait he painted at about the same time. There were a number of artists working under Cortona at the villa, including his later rival, Andrea Sacchi, and Andrea Camassei, Domenichino's pupil, but Cortona himself executed the frescoes of the chapel and various frescoes of the Gallery, including the *Offering to Pomona*. The marchese himself prescribed the program of the decoration of the Gallery, which in keeping with the country setting was devoted to such rural deities as Ceres, Bacchus, Pan, and Pomona, the Roman goddess of fruit, especially that growing on trees. The Morgan drawing, which is still on Jonathan Richardson's mount, was properly attributed to Cortona by the early English collector.

There are a number of changes between the drawing and the frescoed composition, chief among them the reduction in scale of the figure of the goddess and her placement farther into the background. The reduction seems already anticipated in the *pentimento* observable in the head and shoulder line of the figure. The small fruit eater was also moved to the opposite side of the composition, and another child is shown seated near the altar. Accessories like the altar and the baskets of fruit vary somewhat between sketch and fresco. The grace of the composition is much more apparent today in the drawing than in the repainted fresco. Briganti (p. 180) lists five other preparatory drawings for the frescoes of the Gallery, at Windsor (no. 4515), the Uffizi (3030 Santarelli), the Royal Institute of Architects, London (two drawings), and at Rome in a private collection. Walter Vitzthum points out that there is a copy of the Morgan drawing in the Berlin Print Room (Zweite Garnitur, no. 20988, as Gabbiani).

PROVENANCE: Jonathan Richardson Senior (Lugt 2184); Earl of Aylesford (Lugt 58); Charles Fairfax Murray; purchased by J. Pierpont Morgan in London, 1910.

BIBLIOGRAPHY: Briganti, *Cortona*, p. 309.

The Pierpont Morgan Library
No. IV, 173c

55 *St. Catherine of Alexandria*

Red chalk. 8 11/16 × 5 7/8 inches (22.1 × 14.9 cm.). Lined.

Inscribed on verso in pen and brown ink, *N.º 149.; Pietro da Cortona.*

Study for the kneeling figure of St. Catherine of Alexandria, who appears in the right foreground of Cortona's altarpiece representing the Virgin with St. John the Baptist, St. Peter, St. Catherine of Alexandria, and St. Felix of Cantalice, now in the Brera, Milan (repr. Briganti, *Cortona*, fig. 119). The style of the picture and the presence of the Capuchin Felix of Cantalice led Briganti to date it about 1630–1631, when Cortona supplied an altarpiece representing St. Paul Healing Ananias for the new Capuchin church of S. Maria della Concezione in Rome, where the body of Felix of Cantalice is preserved. This relatively early figure study has an old-fashioned, rather Sienese air, but the luminous use of chalk looks forward to Cortona's splendid studies for the Palazzo Pitti.

PROVENANCE: Erasmus Philipps; Richard Philipps, 1st Lord Milford (Lugt S. 2687); Sir John Philipps.

BIBLIOGRAPHY: Briganti, *Cortona*, pp. 194, 309, fig. 118.

EXHIBITIONS: Columbia, S.C., Scholz Exhibition, 1961, no. 29.

Janos Scholz

56 *Nymphs Carving on Trees*

Red chalk. 14 15/16 × 10 1/8 inches (38 × 25.7 cm.). The paper has darkened to brown through exposure. Lined.

Inscribed on mount in pen and red ink, *Carlo Cignani*; on verso of lining in pen and brown ink at upper center, *N. 1/I believe this to be of Pietro da Cortona. As for Carlo Cignani/wee have so little of Him 'tis hard to judge of his hand./ J. Richardson*; at lower right, *the 15th night/Lot 66*; in pencil at lower right, *4-4/A true/P. de Cortona/A. Pond.*

The fact that the nymphs employ the left hand to carve the trunks of the great trees indicates that the composition in its final form would presumably have been reversed to show the normal right-handed movement. Such a reversal would occur in the engraving process, but no engraving of the design has ever been traced although it clearly would have been effective as the frontispiece of a work like G. B. Ferrari's *De Florum Cultura* of 1633 (see No. 57 below) or his *Hesperides* of 1644, for which Cortona supplied a number of the illustrations. Vitzthum suggests a date in the early 1630s for the drawing, even prior to the designs for *De Florum Cultura*. The impressive array of famous collectors' marks the sheet has accumulated bespeaks the esteem in which it has justly been held through the centuries.

PROVENANCE: Peter Lely (Lugt 2092); P. H. Lankrink (Lugt 2090); Jonathan Richardson Senior (Lugt 2184); Arthur Pond (Lugt 2038); Earl of Aylesford (Lugt 58); Charles Fairfax Murray; purchased by J. Pierpont Morgan in London, 1910.

BIBLIOGRAPHY: Fairfax Murray, IV, no. 173, repr.; Briganti, *Cortona*, p. 309.

The Pierpont Morgan Library
No. IV, 173

57 *The Triumph of Nature over Art*

Pen and brown ink, brown wash, over black chalk. 7⅞ × 5 13/16 inches (20 × 14.7 cm.).

Inscribed on verso in pen and brown ink, *Pietro da Cortona*.

Design for one of the illustrations for a treatise on gardening by a learned Jesuit, Giovanni Battista Ferrari. This book, *De Florum Cultura*, appeared in Rome in 1633, with Cortona's design engraved in reverse by Johann Friedrich Greuter; and an Italian translation, in which the same illustration was used, appeared in 1638. The artist illustrates an allegorical passage in Ferrari's text that tells of a contest between Nature and Art. Art, kneeling at the right with grafting knife in hand, has produced a rose bush with flowers of three colors, but Flora is about to crown Nature, who stands pointing at the miracle of her own doing. As if by magic a Chinese rose tree has sprung from the ground. Vertumnus dances holding a sistrum aloft, and three boys, Lucifer, Meriggio, and Hesper (identified respectively by a lily branch, a rose, and a bleeding heart, and representing Dawn, Noon, and Evening) circle the tree while its flowers change from white, to pink, to scarlet, as they are said to do in the course of a day. The wonders of Nature are seen to be more marvelous than those of Art. A drawing by Cortona for another illustration in Ferrari's book is in the Prado at Madrid (repr.

Blunt and Cooke, *Roman Drawings at Windsor*, p. 76, fig. 57).

PROVENANCE: Dr. Alfred Ritter von Wurzbach-Tannenberg (Lugt 2587); Anton Schmid (Lugt S. 2330b); sale, Munich, May 17–18, 1956, no. 30; Mathias Komor (Lugt S. 1882a); purchased by the Metropolitan Museum in New York, 1961.

BIBLIOGRAPHY: J. Bean, *Metropolitan Museum of Art Bulletin*, January 1962, repr. p. 162, fig. 5; Bean, *100 European Drawings*, no. 32, repr.

The Metropolitan Museum of Art
Rogers Fund, 61.2.1

58 *Allegory in Honor of Cardinal Antonio Barberini the Younger*

Pen and brown ink, brown wash, heightened with white, over black chalk, on brown paper. 20½ × 30 inches (52 × 77.2 cm.). Drawing made up of two sheets of paper joined vertically at left of center; pasted corrections at left (including figure of Mercury) and at right (including old man holding book). Repaired hole at lower center; vertical crease at center.

Inscribed in pen and brown ink at lower left, *Incidat* (and illegible monogram); at lower right, *Incidatur commutato Regno* . . . (rest illegible) *inatia*.

The high finish of this large and elaborate drawing, as well as the two inscriptions beginning *Incidat . . .*, in the hand of an ecclesiastical censor, indicate that it was intended for the engraver, and indeed the design was reproduced in the same dimensions but in reverse by a Dutch contemporary of Cortona, Theodor Matham, who was in Rome in the mid-1630s, a date that accords well with the style of Cortona's drawing. Unfortunately the engraving does not bear a dedicatory inscription that might help us in the interpretation of the allegorical message of the subject. Hollstein (*Dutch and Flemish Etchings, Engravings and Woodcuts*, XI, Amsterdam, n.d., p. 252, no. 28) supplies an obviously incorrect title, *The Three Fates in a Colonnade*, but the always knowledgeable Mariette, in a manuscript description of the Albertina's impression of the print, has given us the key to the subject: "Des femmes représentant les diverses parties des Mathématiques venant faire hommage de leurs Sciences dans un Temple où au milieu une femme qui a près d'elle les armes de la famille Barberini est assise au-dessus d'un piédestal au pied duquel sont deux figures de Fleuves qui désignent le Tibre et l'Arno; pièce allégorique à la gloire du cardinal Antoine Barberini dont le portrait est soutenu en l'air par des enfants." In the drawing it is difficult to identify the portrait head, a generic Cortonesque type, but in Matham's engraving the medallion contains an easily recognizable portrait of Antonio Barberini the Younger as a man in his late twenties (for portraits of Antonio, created cardinal in 1627 at the age of nineteen by his uncle, Urban VIII, see A. Nava Cellini, *Paragone*, XVII, no. 191, 1966). Antonio the Younger shared the Barberini penchant for the arts and sciences, and for self-glorification, so it is not surprising that he should have commissioned this allegorical homage from Pietro da Cortona, then at work on the great ceiling fresco in the Barberini palace (see No. 59 below). Mariette was noncommittal about the identity of the female figure seated on the pedestal flanked by the Tiber (with Romulus and Remus) and the Arno (with the Florentine lion, *il marzocco*), allusions to the Tuscan past and Roman present of the Barberini family. This allegorical figure seated next to Antonio the Younger's arms, a shield bearing three bees and surmounted by a cardinal's hat, still has to be explained, as does the presence of a statue of Mercury in the background at the left. The scientific equipment carried by the figures on the right is more readily identifiable in the engraving: the woman leading the procession holds a celestial sphere, her follower bears an armillary sphere, the kneeling female holds tablets inscribed with terrestrial maps, while the old man holds a tablet bearing what appear to be the measurements of a column. Behind them stands Fame, holding a trumpet and a crown of foliage.

This large drawing is made up of two sheets joined vertically somewhat to the left of center. The white highlights employed in the two sections differ; on the right they are softer, on the left harder. It should be noted that the wing and the legs of the flying putto that project over the vertical joining have been reworked in the whites used otherwise only in the left section. This suggests that the client or ecclesiastical censor having found the original left section of the design unsatisfactory, it was cut off, a new solution supplied, and the joining of the two sheets smoothed over by the reworking of the putto in the white used in the new left half. Such a revision and reconsolidation of the design would account for the presence of the ecclesiastical permissions to engrave that appear at both lower left and lower right.

PROVENANCE: Helen Elizabeth Harrison, Maiano, near Florence (purchased by her in S. Gimignano, about 1925); Gilbert Barker, Twyford, Berkshire (inherited from his aunt, Miss Harrison, at her death in 1958); purchased by the Metropolitan Museum in London, 1964.

The Metropolitan Museum of Art
Rogers Fund, 64.50

59 *Woman Holding the Papal Tiara*

Black and red chalk. 8 11/16 × 10 7/8 inches (22 × 27.7 cm.). Foxed; lower corners trimmed. Lined.

One of Cortona's greatest and most original achievements as a painter was the vast ceiling fresco of the Gran Salone or Great Hall of the Palazzo Barberini in Rome, on which he probably began work in the autumn of 1632 and which he completed in 1639. Remarkably enough, of the numerous preparatory drawings such an undertaking must have entailed, only about a dozen have so far been reported in the literature. In addition to those in the Uffizi, the British Museum, the Ashmolean Museum, and a French private collection that Briganti listed in his monograph, Vitzthum in his review of this work (*Burlington Magazine*, CV, 1963, p. 216) cites the previously published or known drawings at Haarlem, Munich, and Ottawa; his assessment of the Briganti list as "very incomplete" indicates that his projected study of Cortona's drawings will add others like the Louvre Inv. 531 (no. 22 of the exhibition "Dessins romains du XVII siècle," 1959). Of these preparatory drawings, none is more beautiful than this study for the personification of Rome, the floating figure of the woman who holds the papal tiara aloft above the papal keys at the summit of the central panel of the ceiling, which is an elaborate allegory of Divine Providence interwoven with the glorification of the Barberini family. The figure is identified as "Roma" by Rosichino in his pamphlet *Dichiarazione delle pitture della sala de' Signori Barberini in Roma*, published in 1640, the year after the ceiling was finished. (For the latest discussion of the iconography, see the article by Vitzthum in the *Burlington Magazine*, CIII, 1961, pp. 427–433.)

The drawing shows only the upper part of the figure, which appears in its entirety in the fresco, and there are as well a number of minor but carefully considered changes. Cortona eventually altered the position of the right hand, which disappears behind the tiara in the fresco, whereas in the drawing it is shown grasping the lower edge of the crown in a gesture of true support, as if the artist might have had a model before him. The new position in the painting, on the other hand, frees the opening of the papal tiara as would be required in the actual act of crowning. The position of the lappets of the crown are also slightly modified in the painting, a change again perhaps dictated by an urge for functional accuracy, since the gracefully straying lappet at the left of the drawing would have to be held back if the crown were thought of as actually being put in place. The billowing draperies of the fresco are only suggested by a few open swirls of the chalk, enhancing the feeling of airiness that is less apparent in the ceiling figure.

One would assume that the Morgan drawing was executed not too long after the artist had settled on the overall scheme of the ceiling. The light flush of color provided by the knowing accents of red chalk is unusual, but not to be doubted as the artist's own.

PROVENANCE: Robert Udney (Lugt 2248); Thomas Banks (Lugt 2423); probably Mrs. Lavinia Forster and Ambrose Poynter; Edward J. Poynter (Lugt 874); Poynter sale, London, Sotheby's, April 24, 1918, no. 31, repr. (as Ludovico Carracci); Earl of Harewood; sale, London, Christie's, July 6, 1965, no. 123, repr., bought by the Morgan Library.

BIBLIOGRAPHY: *Vasari Society*, first series, VI, 1910–1911, pl. 14 (as Ludovico Carracci); Tancred Borenius, "Drawings and Engravings by the Carracci," *Print Collector's Quarterly*, IX, 1922, p. 112, repr. p. 109; "Old Master Drawings in the Collection of Viscount Lascelles," *Apollo*, I, 1925, pp. 192–193, repr. (as Ludovico Carracci); S. von Below, *Beiträge zur Kenntnis Pietro da Cortonas*, Munich, 1932, p. 107; Charles de Tolnay, *History and Technique of Old Master Drawings*, New York, 1943, pp. 122–123, fig. 108; *Dessins romains du XVII siècle* (exhibition catalogue), Paris, Musée du Louvre, 1959, under no. 22; Briganti, *Cortona*, pp. 203, 307; Morgan Library, *Fourteenth Fellows Report, 1965–1966*, pp. 116–117, repr.

EXHIBITIONS: London, Royal Academy of Arts, 1879, no. 35; London, Burlington Fine Arts Club, "Italian Art of the Seventeenth Century," 1925, pp. 41, 48, no. 9, pl. 17 (apparently the first publication of the Cortona attribution by A. G. B. Russell, who presumably also connected the drawing with the Barberini ceiling); London, Royal Academy, Italian Art, 1930: commemorative drawings catalogue, 1931, no. 302, pl. 253b; London, Royal Academy of Arts, "Seventeenth Century Art in Europe," 1938, no. 421; London, Wildenstein, "Artists in 17th Century Rome," 1955, no. 32; Cambridge, Fitzwilliam Museum, "17th Century Italian Drawings," 1959, no. 29.

The Pierpont Morgan Library
Gift of the Fellows with the special assistance
of Mr. and Mrs. Carl Stern, 1965.16

60 *Study of Two Figures for the Age of Gold*

Black chalk. 12¾ × 9¾ inches (32.3 × 24.7 cm.). Scattered repaired holes and small tears; scattered oil stains. Lined.

In June 1637, Pietro da Cortona, taking a leave of absence from his work on the Barberini ceiling, arrived in Florence and almost immediately began a fresco cycle commissioned by the Grand Duke of Tuscany, Ferdinando II, for the Camera della Stufa in the Palazzo Pitti. The subject of the frescoes, said to have been plotted out by Michelangelo Buonarroti the Younger, is the Four Ages of Man as recounted in Ovid's *Metamorphoses*. However, the pessimistic Ovidian sequence, which moves from the delights of the Age of Gold, through the Silver and Bronze, to the horrors of the Age of Iron, has been reversed in the iconographical program employed by Cortona. History moves forward from the pagan Age of Iron to the Age of Gold; the latter fresco contains a number of symbolic references to a contemporary Florentine event, the marriage of Ferdinando II de' Medici to Vittoria della Rovere (see Walter Vitzthum in *Burlington Magazine*, CIV, 1962, pp. 120–121). Only two of the frescoes, the Ages of Gold and Silver, were completed when Cortona left Florence for Venice in the fall of 1637, but the surviving preparatory drawings for all four of the frescoes form so coherent a stylistic group that the whole cycle must have been planned in detail during the summer of that year. The execution of the frescoes representing the Age of Bronze and the Age of Iron had to await Cortona's return to Florence in 1641, the year in which he began work on the decoration of the state rooms along the façade of the Palazzo Pitti.

This drawing is a study for the couple seated at the left in the *Age of Gold*. In this fresco the young woman crowns the seated youth with a laurel crown of victory, an allusion to the name Vittoria, while putti, laden with branches of oak (*rovere*), advance without disturbing a docile lion (the Florentine *marzocco*)—further references to the Medici–della Rovere marriage symbolized by the youthful couple. In addition to two composition studies, a great many chalk studies for figures in the Ages of Gold and Silver have survived, and they are among the finest Italian figure drawings of the seventeenth century. The present example, comparable to the best sheets in the long series in the Uffizi, came very recently to New York, where it joins a companion drawing (No. 61) already in the possession of Mr. Baker.

PROVENANCE: Sir Joshua Reynolds (Lugt 2364); William Mayor (Lugt 2799); Henry Oppenheimer, London; Oppenheimer sale, London, Christie's, July 10–14, 1936, no. 76; Earl of Harewood; sale, London, Christie's, July 6, 1965, no. 124, repr.

BIBLIOGRAPHY: Tancred Borenius, "Drawings and Engravings by the Carracci," *Print Collector's Quarterly*, IX, 1922, p. 114, repr. (as Ludovico Carracci); Campbell, *Cortona*, p. 23; Walter Vitzthum, review of Uffizi Cortona exhibition, *Master Drawings*, IV, no. 1, 1966, p. 63, pl. 40.

Walter C. Baker

61 *Study of a Seated Youth for the Age of Gold*

Black chalk. 11¼ × 10¼ inches (28.6 × 26 cm.). Losses at upper margin. Lined.

Inscribed in black chalk at lower right, *P. Cortona*; illegible inscription in pen and brown ink at lower left.

Preparatory study for the youth seated on the left in Cortona's fresco representing the Age of Gold (see No. 60 above). The position of the youth's right arm is closer in the previous drawing to the solution adopted in the fresco, but in both figure

studies his left arm (here only lightly indicated) is raised, while in the fresco it rests across his chest.

PROVENANCE: John Skippe; his descendants, the Martin family, including Mrs. A. D. Rayner-Wood; Edward Holland Martin; Skippe sale, London, Christie's, November 20–21, 1958, no. 40, pl. 6.

BIBLIOGRAPHY: *Vasari Society*, first series, II, 1906–1907, no. 17, repr. (as Ludovico Carracci); Claus Virch, *Master Drawings in the Collection of Walter C. Baker*, New York, 1962 [privately printed], no. 33, repr.; Briganti, *Cortona*, p. 308; Campbell, *Cortona*, p. 23.

EXHIBITIONS: London, Burlington Fine Arts Club, "Italian Art of the Seventeenth Century," 1925, no. 3 of the drawings catalogue, pl. XII (as Ludovico Carracci); London, Royal Academy, Italian Art, 1930; commemorative drawings catalogue, 1931, no. 301, pl. CCLIII A; Birmingham Museum and Art Gallery, "Commemorative Exhibition of the Art Treasures of the Midlands," 1934, no. 204; London, Royal Academy of Arts, "Seventeenth Century Art in Europe," 1938, no. 419; New York, M. Knoedler, "Great Master Drawings of Seven Centuries. Benefit Exhibition for Columbia University," 1959, no. 33, pl. XXXV; Poughkeepsie, Vassar College/New York, Wildenstein, "Centennial Loan Exhibition. Drawings and Watercolors from Alumnae and their Families," 1961, no. 38, repr.

Walter C. Baker

62 *Study for the Age of Bronze*

Pen and brown ink over black chalk. 9¼ × 6¾ inches (23.5 × 17.2 cm.). Lined.

Numbered in pen and brown ink at lower margin, *n⁰ 5* (rest illegible).

Pietro da Cortona's *Age of Bronze* in the Camera della Stufa of the Palazzo Pitti at Florence represents a scene of Roman military triumph. The composition is dominated at the right by an enthroned general, who from a high pedestal distributes crowns to victorious legionaries. In the left foreground three enchained prisoners crouch dejectedly, while behind them a bearded figure explains the meaning of an inscribed tablet to onlookers gathered before a circular temple that shelters a statue of Christ blessing.

Six composition studies by Cortona for this fresco have been identified, five of them only very recently. All of them, on stylistic grounds, seem to date from 1637, during Cortona's first campaign in the Camera della Stufa, and not from 1641, when the *Age of Bronze* was finally painted (see No. 60 above). If we follow the artist's progress from first ideas to the nearly final solution, the sequence of the six drawings would seem to be: a pen sketch in an album of drawings by Cortona and Ciro Ferri on the New York art market a few years ago; a drawing in the Uffizi on the verso of a design for the façade of Cortona's Roman church of SS. Martina e Luca, begun about 1635 (repr. *Kunstchronik*, XVI, 1963, p. 104); drawings in Munich and Prague (repr. *Burlington Magazine*, CIII, 1961, pp. 425 and 423 respectively); the present drawing; then the following drawing (No. 63). The present sheet deals only with the principal protagonists in the composition, the general distributing crowns to soldiers. There are three conspicuous variations between drawing and fresco: in the latter the general is seated, not standing; the soldier at the center raises his arms to seize the offered crown instead of bending forward humbly; and the captive at the right foreground has been suppressed. In the following drawing, a design for the whole composition, we still encounter the modest attitude of the central soldier and the captive guarded by a lictor in the right foreground, both motifs that disappear in the fresco, but the general is already enthroned and the seated captives seen at the left in the fresco make their appearance for the first time. In the fresco Cortona made a number of changes in the grouping of the figures and in architectural details. Even more advanced composition drawings must have existed, but for the present No. 63 brings us as close as we can come, in the sequence of drawings, to the finished work.

PROVENANCE: Professor J. Isaacs, London; Isaacs sale, London, Sotheby's, February 27, 1964, part of no. 64, bought by the Metropolitan Museum.

BIBLIOGRAPHY: Walter Vitzthum, "Pietro da Cortona's Drawings for the Pitti Palace at the Uffizi," *Burlington Magazine*, CVII, 1965, p. 526, repr. p. 523, fig. 36.

The Metropolitan Museum of Art
Rogers Fund, 64.48.2

63 *Study for the Age of Bronze*

Pen and brown ink, brown wash, over black chalk. 15 15/16 × 10 5/8 inches (40.5 × 27 cm.). All four corners replaced; repairs at left and right margins; scattered repaired holes and tears. Lined.

See No. 62 above.

BIBLIOGRAPHY: Walter Vitzthum, "Pietro da Cortona's Drawings for the Pitti Palace at the Uffizi," *Burlington Magazine*, CVII, 1965, p. 526, fig. 37.

Walter C. Baker

64 *A Wind God*

Black chalk, heightened with white, on brownish paper. 7 7/16 × 13 1/8 inches (18.9 × 33.3 cm.). The irregular edge of sheet has been filled in at all sides.

A study for the figure of a wind god who appears at the edge of the central oval of the frescoed ceiling in the Sala di Apollo, Palazzo Pitti, Florence. It was in 1641 that Pietro da Cortona undertook the decoration of the state rooms on the façade of the Pitti, using an iconographic program that dedicated each room to a planet symbolic of the virtues required of a prince, from youth through old age. The Sala di Venere was the first to be finished, then the Sala di Giove and the Sala di Marte. Work on the elaborate stucco ornament of the Sala di Apollo may have begun as early as 1642 or 1643, but when Cortona left for Rome in 1647 the frescoes in this room were unfinished. Cortona himself was never able to return to Florence to complete the task, and the decoration was finished by his principal assistant, Ciro Ferri, as late as 1660. Vitzthum has remarked that the advanced style of this drawing suggests that it may have been made by Cortona in Rome and sent to Ferri in Florence to guide him in his work. He has further pointed out that an early design by Cortona (Rome, Farnesina, no. 124327) for the Sala di Apollo ceiling, without the wind god, bears on the verso a sketch of this figure, which thus must have been invented by the artist in the first stages of his plans for the decoration. Other drawings by Cortona for the Sala di Apollo are in the Uffizi and the Louvre.

PROVENANCE: George Hibbert; Nathaniel Hibbert; Sir Henry Thurston Holland, 1st Viscount Knutsford and his heirs; sale, London, Sotheby's, April 11, 1935, no. 78; L. G. Duke, London; purchased by the Metropolitan Museum in London, 1961.

BIBLIOGRAPHY: J. Bean, *Metropolitan Museum of Art Bulletin*, January 1962, repr. p. 159, fig. 2; Briganti, *Cortona*, p. 307, no. 53, pl. 287 (the fresco pls. 231–234); Walter Vitzthum, "Pietro da Cortona" (review of Briganti's monograph), *Master Drawings*, I, no. 2, 1963, p. 50; Bean, *100 European Drawings*, no. 33, repr.; Campbell, *Cortona*, p. 20.

EXHIBITIONS: Leicester Museum and Art Gallery, "Old Master Drawings," 1952, no. 26; London, Royal Academy of Arts, "Drawings by Old Masters," 1953, no. 151.

The Metropolitan Museum of Art
The Elisha Whittelsey Collection, 61.129.1

65 *Madonna and Child with St. Martina*

Pen and brown ink, brown wash, over black chalk. 9¾ × 12⅜ inches (24.7 × 31.6 cm.). Spots of red wash at upper left. Partially lined.

Inscribed in pen and brown ink at lower right, *P. da Corton* and *n*⁽ (rest of inscriptions have been cut off).

Pietro da Cortona had a particular devotion to the Roman virgin and martyr Martina, whose name was assigned to the body accidentally discovered in 1634 during excavations in the crypt of the church of the Academy of St. Luke, where Cortona was building his own tomb. He painted at least four devotional pictures representing Martina, identified by her attribute, a long curved two-pronged fork, as she kneels before the Virgin. Two versions are in the Louvre, one in the Academy at Perugia (Briganti, *Cortona*, pls. 219, 244, and 241 respectively), but in composition this hitherto unpublished drawing comes closest to a small picture formerly in the Normanton collection and now belonging to Mr. and Mrs. Harold M. Landon in New York (Briganti, *Cortona*, p. 242, no. 103, not repr.). Briganti dates all these pictures in the mid-1640s, a plausible dating for the drawing as well. In the Uffizi there is a drawing (2994 Santarelli) that corresponds almost exactly to the Landon picture; Briganti rightly dismissed this sheet as an old copy.

PROVENANCE: F. Gawet; C. Wiesboeck; I. Novák; Gustav Nebehay, Berlin.

BIBLIOGRAPHY: *Die Zeichnung*, IV, *Zeichner der Italienischen Kunst*, foreword by Oskar Fischel, Kunsthandlung Gustav Nebehay, Berlin, n.d., no. 121, repr.

Benjamin Sonnenberg

66 *Angels Sealing the Foreheads of the Children of Israel*

Brush and gray wash, heightened with white, over black chalk, on brownish paper. 16¾ × 44⅝ inches (42.6 × 113.2 cm.). The drawing is made up of five sheets of paper joined vertically.

In 1652 Cortona was at work on cartoons for the mosaic decoration of the first three bays in the right nave of St. Peter's. For the elliptical cupolas of these bays he supplied scenes from the Apocalypse—the mosaic of the third cupola representing the Incensing of the Fiery Altar, that of the second the Adoration of the Lamb. These two mosaics had been completed by the time he began, in 1668, the cartoons for the cupola of the first bay, representing Angels Sealing the Foreheads of the Children of Israel (Revelation 7), but the mosaic of this last subject was finished only after Cortona's death, under the supervision of Ciro Ferri (Briganti, *Cortona*, pp. 252–253). This large drawing, made up of several sheets of paper joined vertically, gives us the essential narrative passages of Cortona's highly original rendering of the apocalyptic vision, and the opening of the oval lantern is indicated in black chalk at the upper center of the design. Here, at the end of his career, the artist's draughtsmanship is wonderfully free and self-assured; the pen is abandoned, and brush with wash suffices to indicate the dramatic movement of the figures. No other drawings for these mosaics appear to have survived, but in style and technique this design may be compared with a study in the British Museum (1959–5–9–1) for the *Martyrdom of St. Martina*, a late picture now in the Siena Pinacoteca. An engraving of the mosaic cupola in the first bay by F. Aquilla, published in 1696, names Ciro Ferri as the designer of the composition, but the testimony of this drawing, certainly by Cortona, makes it clear that Ferri's role was limited to supervising the completion of his master's project.

PROVENANCE: Sale, London, Sotheby's, March 13, 1957, no. 16; sale, London, Sotheby's, July 7, 1966, no. 2, repr., bought by the Metropolitan Museum.

The Metropolitan Museum of Art
Rogers Fund, 66.134.1 a–c

Gian Lorenzo Bernini

Naples 1598–Rome 1680

67 *Portrait of a Youth (Self-Portrait?)*

Black and red chalk, heightened with white chalk, on buff paper. 12⁷⁄₁₆ × 9¹⁄₁₆ inches (31.6 × 23 cm.). Several small losses in face, and larger ones near right edge.

Inscribed in pencil in a relatively modern hand at lower right, *da Cav. Bernini.*

In tentatively proposing that the lively countenance of the youth in this impressive portrait represents the features of Bernini himself, Zeri compared the drawing with the presumed self-portraits at Windsor and in the British Museum (Brauer and Wittkower, pls. 1–2), and suggested a date of about 1618 for the Avnet portrait. Attention should also be drawn to the more striking resemblance to the portrait in the Brera at Milan, which Wittkower has put forth as the earliest self-likeness of the artist, dating it about 1610–1612 (*Burlington Magazine*, XCIII, 1951, p. 55, fig. 16). While the youth in the Avnet drawing appears to be somewhat older than the subject of the Brera portrait, they do seem to share a basic physiognomic likeness—even expression. Assuming the boy in the Brera portrait to be between twelve and fourteen years old, and the Avnet youth several years further into his teens, one would arrive at a date of about 1614 or 1615 for the present drawing.

BIBLIOGRAPHY: *Art News*, LVII, no. 4, 1958, p. 17, repr.; Federico Zeri, "Gian Lorenzo Bernini: Un marmo dimenticato e un disegno," *Paragone*, IX, no. 115, 1959, pp. 63–64, pl. 42.

EXHIBITIONS: New York, Wildenstein, "A Comprehensive Exhibition of Drawings and Watercolors," 1958, no. 14.

Mr. and Mrs. Lester F. Avnet

68 *Portrait of Cardinal Scipione Borghese*

Red chalk and graphite. 9¹³⁄₁₆ × 7¹⁄₄ inches (25.3 × 18.4 cm.). Stained. Lined.

Inscribed on verso of lining in pencil in a modern hand at upper left corner, *Lot 223-8-22/265*; in pen and brown ink in the hand of one of the Richardsons (probably Richardson Senior) at top, *Card. Scipio Borghese Nephew of P. Paul V | The Bust is in the Villa Borghese made when | Bernini was very young, but is nevertheless much | esteemed*; in the same

hand, below, partially cut, —*lo stesso Bernini, che un giorno vi fu col Card. Antonio Barberino, dopo qua | . . . vederle proruppe in q̄te parole: Oh quanto poco profitto à fatto io nell'arte della Sco . . . | ingo corso di anni, mentre io conosco, che da fanciullo maneggiano il marino in questo mo . . . | Baldinucci nella sua Vi . . .*; in pencil in C. Fairfax Murray's hand, a translation of the above, across the center, *Bernini when one day with Cardinal Antº Barberini after— | observing it broke out in these words, "How little progress I have made | in sculpture | in the long course of years, when I see that as a boy I managed the | marble in this manner" | Baldinucci | Life of Bernini | coll: Richardson sr | Lawrence*; in pen and brown ink at lower right, *the 12th night | Lot 41.*

The essence of the man and the animation of the moment are mirrored in this extraordinary study from life, truly a speaking likeness of the powerful cardinal who was such a munificent patron of the arts. The drawing, probably one of several executed in the presence of the cardinal, was made in preparation of the over-life-size marble portrait bust that Bernini executed in 1632. It is apparently the only unquestioned example of its kind, that is, the only known surviving life study relating to one of the many portrait busts that Bernini created, although other drawings of the kind certainly were made. There were, for example, the sketches and studies that Chantelou reports Bernini repeatedly made of Louis XIV in anticipation of his execution of the royal bust now in Versailles; mentioned under the date of June 23, 1665, is the fact that Bernini "a dessiné une tête de face, une de profil" (*Journal du voyage en France du Cavalier Bernin par Chantelou*, preface by G. Charensol, Paris, 1930, p. 52; see also pp. 50, 55–56, 66, 73, 111). He must undoubtedly have also drawn the cardinal full face.

As is well known from the accounts of Baldinucci (*Vita di Gian Lorenzo Bernini*, Milan [1948], p. 77) and Bernini's son Domenico (*Vita del Cavalier Gio. Lorenzo Bernini*, Rome, 1713, pp. 10 ff.), when the bust was nearing completion, a crack appeared across the forehead forcing the sculptor to create a second version, which he did in a miraculously short time, two weeks according to Baldinucci, only three days according to the loyal son. Both busts are still in the cardinal's villa on the Pincio in Rome, now the Borghese Gallery, along with the *Apollo and Daphne* and the other great sculptures that Bernini made for him.

The drawing is characterized by an intimacy that is not present in the bust where, despite its animation, the sense of official idealizing portraiture prevails. The marble shows the sitter robust and vital, the host of the splendid banquets, the well-born churchman, the princely collector; the drawing reflects the time-mellowed private man—the cardinal died the following year on October 3, 1633 —relaxed and amiable in the company of the artist he had known and patronized since Bernini was in his teens. The most famous of the other artists of the period whom Scipione Borghese employed was Guido Reni, whose celebrated *Aurora* (1613) was painted for the ceiling of the cardinal's *casino* in the garden of the Palazzo Montecavallo (later Rospigliosi-Pallavicini).

It is interesting that Bernini uses graphite—rather than the more usual black chalk—in combination with the red chalk in which the drawing is in the main executed. For finished independent portrait drawings like that of Sisinio Poli (No. 69 below), he seems to have preferred the more usual combination of red and black chalks. The richness of the textural effects of the graphite are skillfully exploited in the rendering of the hair and beard. Bernini may have become familiar with graphite in his architectural work; the medium was not commonly used until later in the seventeenth century.

PROVENANCE: Jonathan Richardson Senior (Lugt 2184); Sir Thomas Lawrence (Lugt 2445); Sale of a Well-known Amateur (Hope, according to Lugt, *Répertoire des ventes*; Brooke, according to the Fairfax Murray Notebooks), London, Sotheby's, June 20, 1891, no. 185; Charles Fairfax Murray; purchased by J. Pierpont Morgan in London, 1910.

BIBLIOGRAPHY: Fairfax Murray, IV, no. 176, repr.; Brauer and Wittkower, pp. 29, 30, 156, pl. 11; Rudolf Wittkower, *Gian Lorenzo Bernini, The Sculptor of the Roman Baroque*, London, 1955, pp. 15, 195, pl. 52; Howard Hibbard, *Bernini*, Harmondsworth, England, 1965, p. 93, pl. 46.

The Pierpont Morgan Library
No. IV, 176

69 *Portrait of Sisinio Poli*

Black, red, and white chalk on light brown paper. 10%₆ × 8⅛ inches (26.8 × 20.7 cm.). Stained. Lined.

Accompanied by two inscriptions: one in pen and brown ink on thin wood, and another, on paper, copied in pen and brown ink from the first, and attached below the drawing, *Eques Laurentius Berninus | Die vigesima octava Aprilis 1638 | Delineavit | Effigies Sisinij Poli Anno etatis suae | Decimo octavo.*

The attribution of the drawing and the identification of the sitter go back to an accompanying seventeenth-century inscription written on a thin sheet of wood. At one time this wooden leaf was apparently attached to the drawing, but at some point, probably in the eighteenth century, the leaf was separated from the original mount and its text transcribed more or less accurately on a sheet of paper now pasted to the lower edge of the drawing. The wooden leaf is now mounted on the undermat of the drawing.

While the greater part of the surviving portrait drawings by Bernini are self-portraits—they number at least a dozen—about a half-dozen or so portraits like the present typical example are known. Very likely the sitters were people in Bernini's personal circle. The list of works of art coming from the collection of Cassiano dal Pozzo that Giuseppe Ghezzi made in 1715 included a portrait drawing by Bernini of one Malvezzi and another item described only as a portrait of Mascardi (*Burlington Magazine*, CII, 1960, p. 326, nos. 163 and 140). This last may be identical with or related to the portrait at the École des Beaux-Arts (there catalogued under the name of Federico Zuccaro), which is inscribed *Augustinus Mascardus | Aeques L. Berninus | Delineavit* (Agostino Mascardi, 1590–1640, professor of rhetoric at Genoa and Rome). The inscription *Gio. Pietro Verney* is found on a fine portrait head in the Louvre (Inv. 9596; exhibited in "Dessins romains du XVII siècle," 1959, no. 18), traditionally attributed to Bernini at least since Mariette's time but rejected by Brauer and Wittkower (p. 153, note 1).

The youth holding a broad-brimmed hat against his breast (only the brim is visible) is identified by the inscription as Sisinio Poli, aged eighteen. Possibly he was a member of the same family as Faustus Poli (died 1653), who long served the Barberini family and was made a cardinal by Urban VIII in 1643. Since the inscription specifies the day and month as well as the year when the portrait was made, it may have marked the youth's eighteenth birthday.

PROVENANCE: Charles Fairfax Murray; purchased by J. Pierpont Morgan in London, 1910.

BIBLIOGRAPHY: Fairfax Murray, IV, no. 174, repr.; Brauer and Wittkower, p. 156, pl. 16.

EXHIBITIONS: Detroit, Italy 1600–1700, 1965, no. 28, repr.

The Pierpont Morgan Library
No. IV, 174

70 *Study for the Tomb of Cardinal Domenico Pimentel*

Modeled with the brush in brown wash, over graphite. 14¹³⁄₁₆ × 11¼ inches (37.6 × 28.6 cm.). The intentional mottling of the wash to indicate the variegation of the marble blends somewhat confusingly at the lower left with the abraded areas of damage that the drawing has suffered.

Inscribed on verso in pencil in a relatively modern hand, *Lorenzo Bernini fec.*

The finished marble tomb of the Spanish cardinal, which was executed by the great sculptor's pupils, differs in a number of ways from this preliminary design from the hand of Bernini himself. The cast of characters, however, remains essentially the same in both sketch and marble; the changes involve a general broadening of the stepped base and details of pose and drapery. The over-life-size figures of the cardinal kneeling on the sarcophagus, the group of Charity and her children, and Justice covering her eyes all retain the positions indicated in the drawing, but Bernini ultimately transposed and altered the allegorical figures at the back (on the tomb they can be identified as Faith and Wisdom), and added a putto to support the fasces at Justice's side. The putto was given the general pose, in reverse, of Charity's standing child when that figure's position was changed to a reclining one in the final design.

Wittkower (*Gian Lorenzo Bernini, The Sculptor of the Roman Baroque*, New York, 1955, p. 27) comments on the fact that although the Pimentel tomb is actually a wall tomb, its presentation as a relief against a contrasting marble background creates the illusion of a free-standing monument.

Enggass in the catalogue of the Detroit exhibition of 1965 regarded the Morgan drawing as evidence that Bernini originally envisioned a free-standing tomb, arguing that the allegorical figure behind Justice, who turns away from the observer and is almost hidden by the architectural elements, would be meaningful only as a member of a free-standing monument. While this is a logical argument, it should not be overlooked that the light graphite lines at the upper left and right of the sheet already indicate the outlines of the marble inset of the background wall as it appears in the actual tomb setting. The fact that the wash is somewhat muddied in the area of the background figure on the right would seem to show that the artist experienced difficulty at this point and was made aware that more space was required to accommodate the rear allegorical figures.

Cardinal Pimentel died in 1653 shortly after receiving his cardinal's hat. His tomb was probably commissioned soon afterward. Antonio Raggi carved the figure of Charity, G. A. Mari that of Justice, and Ercole Ferrata the cardinal's image and the background figures of Wisdom and Faith. Brauer and Wittkower (pl. 39) identified a sheet of sketches among the large group of Bernini's drawings at Leipzig as Bernini's studies for the latter figure.

PROVENANCE: Probably B. Jolles (Lugt S. 381a); purchased by the Morgan Library in London, 1958.

BIBLIOGRAPHY: *Morgan Library, Ninth Fellows Report, 1958–1959*, p. 97; Walter Vitzthum, review of Detroit exhibition, *Master Drawings*, III, no. 4, 1965, p. 407.

EXHIBITIONS: Detroit, Italy 1600–1700, 1965, no. 29, repr.

The Pierpont Morgan Library
Gift of the Fellows, 1958.18

71 *Caricature*

Pen and brown ink. 8⅛ × 5⅝ inches (20.7 × 14.4 cm.). Three horizontal creases across top, center, and bottom. Lined.

As a formal portraitist, Bernini seems to have found the making of caricatures an amusing outlet, and they once must have existed in some number. His son Domenico owned an entire album of them, which he presented to Antonio la Cloche, General of the Dominican Order. Although the subject of the present example is nameless, Bernini's caricatures appear to be among the earliest known of specific personalities. (Domenichino's caricature at Chatsworth of a member of the Aldobrandini household is another early specimen. See *Burlington Magazine*, XCIV, 1952, p. 169, fig. 15.) If the identification of the head of a bejowled cardinal in the Vatican Library as Scipione Borghese (Brauer and Wittkower, pls. 146–147) is accurate as well as plausible, Bernini appears on occasion to have penned swift drolleries of subjects he was simultaneously immortalizing in marble (cf. No. 68 of the exhibition). The caricature of Cassiano dal Pozzo, discovered by Sir Anthony Blunt in the Boymans-van Beuningen Museum, Rotterdam (*Burlington Magazine*, CII, 1960, pp. 321, 327, fig. 35) is to be added to the Brauer and Wittkower list of surviving caricatures by Bernini at the Corsiniana at Rome, the Vatican Library, and Leipzig. For another slight caricature notation attributed to Bernini, see H. L. Cooke, *Burlington Magazine*, XCVII, 1955, p. 323, fig. 23.

Mr. Scholz states that the present drawing was acquired as one of a group of about eighteen drawings in an album bound in a modern German binding marked *Bolognesische Karikaturen*.

EXHIBITIONS: Scholz Exhibitions: Hagerstown, 1960–1961, no. 41; Columbia, S.C., 1961, no. 6; Hamburg, 1963, no. 18.

Janos Scholz

Daniele Crespi

Milan about 1598–Milan 1630

72 *St. Sebastian*

Black and white chalk on paper tinted reddish-brown. 16⅞ × 9¹³⁄₁₆ inches (42.8 × 24.8 cm.). Slightly extended at lower edge. Numerous losses, breaks, and abrasions, particularly at left and lower margins. Lined.

Traces of obliterated inscription in pen and brown ink at lower center.

In 1629 Crespi completed his major work, the fresco cycle in the Certosa at Garegnano on the outskirts of Milan. A year later, having executed yet another fresco cycle for the Certosa at Pavia, he was dead of the plague, a fact that lends poignancy to this representation of one of the protectors against such a fate. Although possessed of a certain completeness in itself, the drawing presumably was a study for a painting, but none relating to it has been discovered. The detailed inventory of Crespi's possessions at the time of his death mentioned "uno quadro a olio di Santo Sebastiano" (Giorgio Nicodemi, *Daniele Crespi*, Busto Arsizio, 1930, p. 53). A fragment of a painting formerly with Victor Spark in New York, attributed to Daniele Crespi with the concurrence of Roberto Longhi (information on Frick Library photograph 708–3 b), shows the saint in the company of Stephen, Lawrence, and Peter Martyr, but there he is depicted in the standing pose in which he is more usually represented, although in sturdiness of physique the painted figure is not unlike the present realistic study. The expressive head reflects the fervor of the religious atmosphere in Milan where Cardinal Federico Borromeo was carrying on the principles of his uncle S. Carlo Borromeo.

PROVENANCE: Charles Fairfax Murray; purchased by J. Pierpont Morgan in London, 1910.

The Pierpont Morgan Library
No. IV, 37b

Andrea Sacchi

Rome 1599–Rome 1661

73 *Allegory of Divine Wisdom*

Point of brush and brown wash, pen and brown ink, over preliminary indications in red and some black chalk, traces of corrections in white. 12¼ × 13⅛ inches (31.2 × 33.3 cm.). Considerable abrasion. Lined.

Inscribed with point of brush above one of the figures at right, *candidezza*; numbered in brown ink at upper left, *277*.

Unlike the usual academic chalk studies commonly associated with Sacchi's style as a draughtsman, this sheet is a free, even rough, working sketch. It represents a preliminary stage in the artist's development of his design for the ceiling of one of the large reception rooms in the Palazzo Barberini, a project completed between 1629 and 1633 and so probably overlapping in its final stages with the commencement of Pietro da Cortona's *Divine Providence* for the ceiling of the Great Hall in the same Roman palace (see No. 59). Complementary in their themes and in their glorification of the Barberini family, the two large allegorical frescoes were diametrically opposed in principle and approach, reflecting the artistic polarities of the period that gave rise to controversy between Sacchi and Cortona and their respective adherents.

Sacchi, a protégé of the Cardinal Antonio Barberini, in illustration of a text from the Apocrypha (Wisdom of Solomon 6:21) represented "Divina Sapienza" enthroned above the world in the company of eleven maidens personifying various qualities of wisdom (see *Die Künstlerbiographien von Giovanni Battista Passeri*, ed. J. Hess, Leipzig and Vienna, 1934, for a full analysis of the subject; also H. Posse, *Der römische Maler Andrea Sacchi*, Leipzig, 1929, p. 39). Despite the summary execution of the drawing, many of these figures are identifiable: at the right, Purity is marked not only by the inscription *candidezza*, but also by the swan she carries; immediately on Divine Wisdom's right is Deity with her golden triangle, then Harmony with the lyre of Apollo, and above and back of her, Eternity holding the circle formed by a serpent holding its own tail in its mouth. The composition of the drawing is much more compact than that of the diffuse fresco (repr. Rudolf Wittkower, *Art and Architecture in Italy, 1600–1750*, 2nd. rev. ed., Baltimore, 1965, pl. 93), where there is a more static alignment of groups and where, in keeping with Sacchi's desire for the classic clarity that he championed, the figure of Divine Wisdom became less animated and was posed more frontally on a large throne with couchant lions.

Thus far, the Cooper Union sheet is the only known drawing for the Barberini fresco, scholars having searched in vain for other studies at Windsor and Düsseldorf where Sacchi is particularly well represented.

PROVENANCE: Giovanni Piancastelli (no mark, see Lugt S. 2078a).

EXHIBITIONS: New York, Cooper Union Museum, "Five

Centuries of Drawing," circulated by the American Federation of Arts, 1959–1961, no. 18.

The Cooper Union Museum
1901–39–1714

Aniello Falcone

Naples about 1600–Naples 1656

74 *The Martyrdom of a Male Saint*

Red chalk. 18⅛ × 12 1/16 inches (46 × 30.6 cm.). Various small spots and tears. Lined.

Inscribed in pen and brown ink at lower margin, *Giordano . . .* (rest illegible).

The eighteenth-century Neapolitan art historian Bernardo De Dominici, a collector who possessed drawings by Falcone, noted that certain of the artist's figure studies were "touched in red chalk so softly that many thought them to be the work of Andrea Sacchi" (*Vite dei pittori, scultori ed architetti napoletani*, III, 1743, p. 74). The present example would seem to justify the confusion; not only is the red chalk draughtsmanship close to and certainly inspired by Sacchi's figure style, but the composition itself is certainly indebted to the Roman artist's clear-cut narrative pictures of the 1630s, particularly to the *Martyrdoms of St. Andrew and of St. Longinus* painted for the crypt of St. Peter's. Falcone's reputation as a painter is based on his battle scenes, and no altarpiece for which this drawing could have been a study is recorded. Attributed in a recent Amsterdam exhibition to Luca Giordano, on the basis of a misleading inscription at the lower margin, the drawing was restored to Falcone by Françoise Coulanges-Rosenberg, who recognized it as the sheet rightly attributed to Falcone in the 1775–1776 Mariette sale, where it is described as: "Un saint assommé de coups de bâton dans Rome; Sujet plein d'expression, fait avec art, à la sanguine." The saint's brutal assailants and the helmeted soldiers in this composition are characteristic Falcone types, and they are drawn in the soft, rather painterly manner that is typical of him.

PROVENANCE: Pierre-Jean Mariette (Lugt 1852); Mariette sale, Paris, 1775–1776, part of no. 398; Marquis de Lagoy

(Lugt 1710); unidentified collector (Lugt 2508); purchased by the Metropolitan Museum in Amsterdam, 1965.

EXHIBITIONS: Amsterdam, Bernard Houthakker, "Dessins," 1961, no. 25 (as Luca Giordano).

The Metropolitan Museum of Art
Rogers Fund, 65.137

75 *Portrait of Masaniello*

Red and white chalk. 8⅞ × 6¹¹⁄₁₆ inches (22.4 × 17 cm.). A few small losses and stains. Lined.

Inscribed in pen and brown ink in an old hand at lower center, *Ritratto di Masaniello*; on verso of lining in the same hand, *questo ritratto di Masaniello | è fatto di mano d'Aniello | falcone Napolitano che fù maestro di Sal^vr. Rosa, | e de battaglisti Napolitani del suo tempo, | come d'Andrea Coppola, di Pepe Piscopo, | d'Andrea de Lione, di Ciccio Napolitano delle | battaglie, e studiato dal P. Cortese Giesuita detto | il P. Borgognone delle battaglie; anche da | M. Angelo delle battaglie, che in quel tempo | era in Napoli, e dipinse il Mercato con li | primi moti di qtta. gran revolusione; quadro | superbissimo in genere suo che hà il Sig. Card. Spada figlio del Sig. M^se. | Horatio; e questo è ritratto simigliantissimo, |perche Anniello falcone era in Napoli nella | revolusione. Era questo disegno in un | libro di disegni ch'io comprai l'anno 1683 | in Napoli da Andrea di Lione decrepito, e mi | disse, che il d°. libro era del Duca di Tarsia | vecchio. | Z*; numbered in pencil in a later hand at upper left, *1448*.

The inscription of collector "Z" (possibly "S.Z." or "Z.S." but apparently not Zaccaria Sagredo), who acquired this drawing in 1683, identified the head as a portrait of Tommaso Aniello, called Masaniello (1622–1647), the Amalfi fisherman who led a revolt among the tax-burdened lower classes against the Spanish governor in Naples in 1647. In making this identification, the collector may have been aware that Falcone, whom he properly identified as the master of Salvator Rosa, was thought to have painted a portrait of Masaniello, as Bernardo De Dominici later noted in his biography of the battle painter in *Vite dei pittori, scultori ed architetti napoletani*, first published in 1742–1743 (1840–1846 ed., III, p. 455). It was the late Professor Saxl who pointed out that Falcone's model for the Morgan drawing was not the young insurrectionist, but Leonardo da Vinci's red chalk study, in Budapest, for one of the figures in the *Battle of Anghiari*. Saxl did not rule out the possibility that the impersonal head might nevertheless have been intended to stand in a general way for the historical

character, represented presumably in the act of haranguing the proletariat. He cited a seventeenth-century engraving in profile and a piece of sculpture representing Masaniello as bearing some resemblance to the drawing, but he also noted that the identical head, draped with a turban, appears in the background of Falcone's *Battle between the Saracens and Latins* in the Prado, Madrid. There may well have been a famous portrait of Masaniello in profile since, in addition to the engraving Saxl mentions and the Morgan "portrait," there is a small etching by Stefano della Bella (De Vesme 363) traditionally supposed to represent Masaniello. It shows a large-nosed young man with mustache and curly sideburns, wearing a close-fitting peaked cap, in type not too far removed from the presumably genuine likeness of Masaniello painted in 1647 by Andrea di Lione (1610-1685), Falcone's pupil, from whom collector "Z" acquired the album of which the Morgan drawing was once a part.

In connection with the early collector's identification of the subject of this sheet, it should perhaps be kept in mind that the closeness of the names "Tommaso Aniello" called "Masaniello," and "Aniello Falcone," might have given rise to some confusion during the interval between Falcone's death in 1656 and the year 1683.

The "Duca di Tarsia," mentioned in the inscription as the original owner of the album, was a patron of Falcone, and the painter at one time resided in his palace.

PROVENANCE: Ferrante Spinelli, Principe di Tarsia; Andrea di Lione; "Z" (Lugt S. 2997c); Sir Thomas H. Crawley-Boevey; Boevey sale, London, Christie's, July 30, 1877 (according to Fairfax Murray's note on mat); Charles Fairfax Murray; purchased by J. Pierpont Morgan in London, 1910.

BIBLIOGRAPHY: Fairfax Murray, I, no. 107, repr.; II, Introduction [pp. 2–3], pl. 68 (translation and reproduction of inscription); Fritz Saxl, "The Battle Scene without a Hero. Aniello Falcone and His Patrons," *Warburg Journal*, III, 1939–1940, pp. 84–85, pl. 15a; Nicola Ivanoff, *I Disegni italiani del seicento. Scuola veneta, lombarda, ligure, napoletana*, Venice [1959], p. 130; Walter Vitzthum, "Neapolitan Seicento Drawings in Florida," *Burlington Magazine*, CIII, 1961, p. 314; Walter Vitzthum, "Le Dessin baroque à Naples," *L'Oeil*, no. 97, 1963, p. 46, repr.

The Pierpont Morgan Library
No. I, 107

Giovanni Benedetto Castiglione

Genoa about 1600–Mantua 1665

76 *God the Father Appearing to Abraham and His Family*

Brush, brown, red, green, blue, and white oil paint on light brown paper. 15³⁄₁₆ × 20⅝ inches (38.6 × 52.4 cm.). Vertical creases at center and at right; all four corners replaced; repaired tear at left. Lined.

In this and the following drawing Castiglione uses a technique of his own invention, working with a brush first dipped in linseed oil, then in coarsely ground pigment without any binding medium. If, as has been suggested, he was attempting to imitate on paper the effect of a Flemish oil sketch on wood (Castiglione is said to have studied under Van Dyck in Genoa), the result he achieved is quite different, for the pigment on paper has a granular quality reminiscent of natural chalk or pastel. The artist's bravura manner is well served by this fluid technique, and he produced a great many such large-scale drawings, which seem to have been intended not as preparatory studies for pictures, but as works of art complete in themselves. Here Castiglione has adapted Raphael's design for the *Appearance of God to Abraham* used in the Vatican Logge, placing the action in a landscape setting where a Corinthian portico at the right and classical architectural fragments at the left strike a picturesquely anachronistic note. Other somewhat smaller versions of this composition, also executed in brush and pigment, are in Berlin (no. 12,511) and at Windsor (Blunt, *Castiglione and Della Bella at Windsor*, no. 61, with mention of a replica in the Misme collection, Paris).

PROVENANCE: Unidentified collector's mark at lower right corner; purchased by the Metropolitan Museum in London, 1965.

EXHIBITIONS: London, P. & D. Colnaghi, "Old Master Drawings," 1965, no. 28, pl. VI.

The Metropolitan Museum of Art
Purchase, Robert Lehman Gift, 65.176

77 *A Youth Playing a Pipe for a Satyr*

Brush, brown, red, green, and blue oil paint. 16 × 21¹⁄₁₆ inches (40.6 × 53.5 cm.). Vertical crease at center. Lined.

A brilliant example in the pastoral vein that was to be so much appreciated in the eighteenth century. Fragonard admired and copied this kind of oil sketch, and his own drawings show the marked influence of Castiglione's example. Here the pigment is even drier and even more suggestive of colored chalk than in the previous drawing. Further brush drawings by Castiglione are to be found in New York in the Suida Manning and the Scholz collections.

PROVENANCE: Sir William Drake (Lugt 736); Drake sale, London, Christie's, May 24–25, 1892, no. 415; Dr. Francis Springell; Springell sale, London, Sotheby's, June 28, 1962, no. 39, repr., bought by the Metropolitan Museum.

BIBLIOGRAPHY: J. Bean, *Metropolitan Museum of Art Bulletin,* March 1963, pp. 235–236, fig. 9; Bean, *100 European Drawings,* no. 34, repr.

EXHIBITIONS: London, Royal Academy of Arts, "Drawings by Old Masters," 1953, no. 136; London, P. & D. Colnaghi, "Drawings by Old Masters from the Collection of Dr. and Mrs. Francis Springell," 1959, no. 53, pl. XIV.

The Metropolitan Museum of Art
Gustavus A. Pfeiffer Fund, 62.126

78 *Fantastic Subject: Five Nude Male Figures Punishing Another*

Pen and brown ink, brown wash. 10³⁄₁₆ × 15⅛ inches (25.9 × 38.4 cm.). Upper and lower right corners replaced; repairs at lower left.

Numbered in pen and light brown ink at lower center, *15*; in another hand at right margin, *24*.

With pen in hand Castiglione was wonderfully inventive. Apparently untrammeled by iconographic convention, he created the *scherzi di fantasia* (fantastic jokes) that enjoyed such a vogue in the eighteenth century, above all in Venice, where both his drawing style and his subject matter were particularly savored. Neither the subject of this nor of the following drawing can be identified; rather than studies for narrative or allegorical compositions, they are brilliant *divertimenti* by one of the most fluent and gifted draughtsmen of seventeenth-century Italy.

PROVENANCE: Purchased by the Metropolitan Museum in London, 1965.

EXHIBITIONS: London, Alpine Club Gallery, "Old Master Drawings Presented by W. R. Jeudwine," 1965, no. 15, pl. VI.

The Metropolitan Museum of Art
Rogers Fund, 65.112.4

79 Fantastic Subject: Five Despairing or Angry Figures

Pen and brown ink, brown wash. 10¼ × 14½ inches (26.1 × 36.7 cm.). Repaired losses at three corners.

Numbered in pen and light brown ink at lower center, *10*; in pen and dark brown ink in another hand at right margin center, *32*.

In the inventory that accompanied the drawings of the Fairfax Murray collection at the time of its acquisition by J. Pierpont Morgan in 1910, this drawing was properly attributed to Castiglione, but in the fourth volume of Fairfax Murray's publication, which appeared in 1912, the English artist and *marchand-amateur* unfortunately rejected what must have been the traditional attribution and classified the drawing as "ascribed to Giordano." It was restored to Castiglione when Robert Manning and Philip Pouncey independently recognized it as one of the artist's strange *capricci*. It seems logical, as Blunt suggested, that drawings of this kind were produced at the same time as the artist's etchings *Melancholy* and *The Genius of G. B. Castiglione*, which are from the period around 1648. Castiglione made a token contribution to seventeenth-century caricature in the small head at the lower right of the sheet.

The Morgan and Metropolitan drawings (see No. 78 above) must have originally been part of an album, as each bears numbers from the same two sequences, i.e., a lightly indicated number at lower center and heavier numerals in a more precise clerical hand at the center of the right margin. There are also related numbers on a drawing in the Victoria and Albert Museum (C.A.I. 829). The numbering at the lower edge is apparently the older numeration, as another drawing in the Louvre (Inv. 9459; *La Revue des Arts*, VIII, 1958, p. 268, fig. 2) of a similar fantastic subject carries only the lightly penned number *17*. Similar numbers are also found on a sheet in the Witt Collection (no. 3845; *Hand-List*, p. 68) and on a drawing formerly in the Skippe collection and now owned by Wilfrid Thesiger (P. & D. Colnaghi, "Old Master Drawings," 1959, no. 22). These numbers near the lower margin seem to be in the same hand as that which inscribed the *26* on one of the Windsor Castiglione drawings (Inv. 3911; Blunt, no. 54), posing the possibility that the sheets under discussion may, like many of the Windsor sheets, ultimately have come from the great collection of Castiglione's drawings owned by Zaccaria Sagredo (1653–1729), Venice.

PROVENANCE: Charles Fairfax Murray; purchased by J. Pierpont Morgan in London, 1910.

BIBLIOGRAPHY: Fairfax Murray, IV, no. 194, repr. (as Luca Giordano); Blunt, *Castiglione and Della Bella at Windsor*, p. 13, note 1.

EXHIBITIONS: Vancouver Art Gallery, "The Nude in Art," 1964, no. 41, repr.

The Pierpont Morgan Library
No. IV, 194

Giovanni Francesco Grimaldi

Bologna 1606–Rome 1680

80 Landscape with a Bridge and Two Figures

Pen and brown ink, brown wash, over traces of black chalk. 13⅞ × 17½ inches (34.1 × 44.5 cm.). Vertical crease at center; crease at lower right corner; various spots. Lined.

All the compositional underpinnings of this landscape, the clump of trees and the reclining figures that establish scale in the foreground, the broad sweep of water that leads diagonally into the middle ground accentuated by a fortified bridge and then on to the lightly indicated hills beyond, are borrowed from Annibale Carracci and Domenichino, Grimaldi's Bolognese models. Such stock landscapes, coarsely but often, as here, competently rendered, are Grimaldi's claim to celebrity as a draughtsman. Some of this fame is reflected glory, for his landscape drawings have been repeatedly attributed to his elders and betters, Annibale and Domenichino. Instructive comparison with authentic landscapes by these two artists (Nos. 10,

28, and 29) may be made on this occasion, and indeed dictated the inclusion of this sample of Grimaldi's style in the exhibition.

PROVENANCE: Unidentified English collector (Lugt S. 416a); purchased by the Metropolitan Museum in London, 1962.

BIBLIOGRAPHY: Walter Vitzthum, "Disegni di Alessandro Algardi," *Bollettino d'Arte*, XLVIII, 1963, p. 82, left half of drawing repr. fig. 16.

The Metropolitan Museum of Art
Rogers Fund, 62.204.1

Francesco Montelatici, called Cecco Bravo

Florence 1607–Innsbruck 1661

81 *A Dream*

Black and red chalk. 11 7/16 × 18 3/8 inches (29 × 46.7 cm.). A few small stains; repaired losses at lower right corner. Lined.

Inscribed on mount in pen and brown ink in an old hand, *Cecco Bravo*; on verso, *S 23*.

This fantasy, in swirling red and black chalks, belongs to the category of the artist's compositions known as his "dreams" from the old inscriptions, possibly in the hand of the Florentine collector and *marchand-amateur* Francesco Maria Nicolò Gabburri (1675–1742), that occur on certain drawings of this kind. Typical inscriptions beginning *Sogno. Di Francesco Montelatici Pittor Fiorentino* . . . are found on the drawings at Oxford (Parker, *Ashmolean Catalogue*, II, no. 917) and in the Leonora Hall Gurley Memorial Collection at the Chicago Art Institute (no. 22.5468). A dream fantasy in the Louvre (Inv. 1348) is inscribed in an eighteenth-century English hand *Ceco Bravo | one of his dreams*.

Parker cites J. A. Gere's reference to the catalogue of the Knapton sale, May 27, 1807, nos. 240–248, where a number of "large dreams . . . very fantastical" are listed and the draughtsman described as a "very prolific genius in the representations of fantastic subjects, which by the Amateurs are called his Dreams . . ."

In conveying a sense of terror and the uncanny, these drawings anticipate the nightmare subjects Henry Fuseli created a little more than a century

later and, like them, they also defy exact interpretation. The Morgan drawing is a good example of the bravura of draughtsmanship that is cited in the old inscriptions as the source of the appellation "Bravo" (Cecco is a diminutive of Francesco).

PROVENANCE: Purchased by the Morgan Library in London, 1958.

BIBLIOGRAPHY: H. M. Calmann [*Catalogue of Drawings*], London [1958], no. 15, repr.; Morgan Library, *Ninth Fellows Report, 1958–1959*, pp. 96–97; Gerhard Ewald, "Studien zur Florentiner Barockmalerei," *Pantheon*, XXIII, 1965, p. 310, fig. 19.

The Pierpont Morgan Library
Gift of the Fellows, 1958.17

82 *Youthful St. John the Baptist*

Red chalk, traces of white chalk. 15 3/4 × 10 inches (40 × 25.4 cm.). Oil stain and repaired loss at lower left; some marginal stains. Watermark: heraldic mountain composed of six hills.

The figure of the Baptist, if disassociated from the crossed staff, might well be counted among Cecco Bravo's remarkable series of nude studies in which he continues, in his own highly individual manner, the long Florentine tradition for this kind of drawing. It retains overtones of his admiration for Andrea del Sarto, after whose works he is known to have made studies. The drawing, one of several of its kind in Mr. Scholz's collection, was first identified as Cecco Bravo's by Philip Pouncey.

The subject of St. John the Baptist was one that the artist drew repeatedly; there are at least seven examples in the Uffizi and a dozen in the Biblioteca Marucelliana, both of these institutions holding large numbers of his drawings. Cecco Bravo is known to have executed glass paintings of St. John the Evangelist and St. John the Baptist for the church of S. Cecilia, Florence, and a painting of St. John in the Wilderness, now all lost (Masetti, *Cecco Bravo*, p. 94, no. 24, p. 102, no. 41).

PROVENANCE: Giovanni Piancastelli (no mark, see Lugt S. 2078a) (as Bugiardini); Mr. and Mrs. Edward Brandegee (no mark, see Lugt S. 1860c).

BIBLIOGRAPHY: Anna Rosa Masetti, *Cecco Bravo*, Venice, 1962, p. 59.

EXHIBITIONS: Oakland, Scholz Exhibition, 1961, no. 53, repr.

Janos Scholz

Pietro Testa

Lucca 1607/1611–Rome 1650

83 Charity

Pen and brown ink, over preliminary indications in graphite. 12⅝ × 10¼ inches (32 × 26 cm.). Large stain in upper left quadrant; several smaller stains; fold line across center with a small loss to right of center. Lined.

This sheet is a preparatory study, in reverse, for Testa's large etching of the subject (Bartsch, XX, p. 223, no. 28). The drawing bears out Testa's reputation as an appealing delineator of children, commented upon by Mariette in his remarks on the Testa drawings in the Crozat sale catalogue (1741), and at the same time exhibits his facility in the representation of landscape motifs.

Testa also etched a similar but less elaborate composition in horizontal format (Bartsch, XX, p. 222, no. 27); his preparatory drawing, formerly in the Mond collection, is now in the Metropolitan Museum, where it is kept with the etching in the Print Room (repr. T. Borenius and R. Wittkower, *Catalogue of the Collection of Drawings . . . Formed by Sir Robert Mond*, London [1937], pl. XLIII, no. 248). It seems logical that the simpler horizontal composition preceded the large vertical etching; Testa dedicated the latter to his fellow citizen Cardinal Gerolamo Bonuisia of Lucca, whose device of the eight-pointed star appears at the center of the lower edge of the print.

PROVENANCE: Charles Fairfax Murray; purchased by J. Pierpont Morgan in London, 1910.

BIBLIOGRAPHY: Fairfax Murray, IV, no. 180, repr.

The Pierpont Morgan Library No. IV, 180

84 The Death of Sinorix
Verso: The Death of Sinorix

Pen and brown ink, brown wash, and black chalk. In addition, some pen and black ink on verso. 8¹³⁄₁₆ × 11¹³⁄₁₆ inches (22.5 × 30 cm.). Repair in upper right corner, apparently by the artist himself; scattered oil stains. Watermark: probably a figure holding a cross, within a shield (cf. Heawood 1350–1352; Briquet 7628).

Numbered in pen and brown ink at lower right, *31*; on verso in pencil at lower left center, *5*.

As Walter Vitzthum pointed out in a clear-cut analysis (*Master Drawings*, II, 1964, pp. 296–299), this sheet is one of an interesting sequence of drawings in which Testa worked out the composition of his etching the *Death of Sinorix* (Bartsch, XX, p. 220, no. 19). The present drawing shows the artist working within the horizontal format of the etching after his earlier experiments with a vertical composition in the drawings in the Berlin Kupferstichkabinett and the British Museum. On the verso of the Morgan drawing, he has reversed the direction in which the horses move. In a drawing at Haarlem, he further experimented with an enlarged crowd of figures. The composition crystallized in the following drawing (No. 85), which, when squared, served as a preparation for the final version in Stockholm. Yet another of Testa's studies for the print, a black chalk *Studies of Horses*, now in the British Museum, was remarked by Popham, who noted that the horses were adapted from those in the antique group of the Dioscorides (*Catalogue of the Drawings in the Collection formed by Sir Thomas Phillipps, Bart., F.R.S., Now in the Possession of T. Fitzroy Phillipps Fenwick . . .* [privately printed], 1935, p. 167, no. 3).

As one of the draughtsmen employed by Cardinal Francesco Barberini's learned secretary, Cassiano dal Pozzo, to record works of ancient art for his *Museum Chartaceum*, Testa was well prepared to cope with details like the statue of Diana and her deer (in the present drawing only roughly sketched in chalk in the center of the composition), the ornament of the chariot, and the circular temple in the following drawing. It may also have been in this archaeological ambience that he came to illustrate the rarely encountered story of Sinorix, which comes from Plutarch's *De mulierum virtutibus*. He represents the moment at which the servitors of the Tetrarch Sinorix carried their dying master to his chariot after he had been poisoned in the Temple of Diana by Camma, the widow of the Tetrarch Sinatus, whom Sinorix had murdered in order to be able to marry her.

A drawing by Testa described as the *Death of Camma* was listed under no. 272 of the Crozat sale catalogue of 1741. A red chalk drawing attributed to Testa in the Louvre (Inv. 1899) appears to be no more than a copy after the print.

PROVENANCE: Sir Thomas Lawrence (Lugt 2445); Sale of a Well-known Amateur [Hope, according to Lugt, *Répertoire des ventes*; Brooke, according to the Fairfax Murray Notebooks], London, Sotheby's, June 20, 1891, part of no. 230; Charles Fairfax Murray; purchased by J. Pierpont Morgan in London, 1910.

BIBLIOGRAPHY: Walter Vitzthum, review of the Berlin exhibition "Entwurf und Ausführung," *Master Drawings*, II, 1964, p. 297, pl. 45.

The Pierpont Morgan Library
No. IV, 180h

85 *The Death of Sinorix*

Pen and brown ink over black chalk. Squared in pen and brown ink. 4 × 5¾ inches (10.1 × 14.6 cm.). Lined.

See No. 84 above.

PROVENANCE: Sir Thomas Lawrence (Lugt 2445); Sale of a Well-known Amateur [Hope, according to Lugt, *Répertoire des ventes*; Brooke, according to the Fairfax Murray Notebooks], London, Sotheby's, June 20, 1891, part of no. 231; Charles Fairfax Murray; purchased by J. Pierpont Morgan in London, 1910.

The Pierpont Morgan Library
No. IV, 180a

Giovanni Battista Salvi, called Sassoferrato

Sassoferrato 1609–Rome 1685

86 *Portrait of a Woman*

Black and white chalk, squared for enlargement in black chalk, on blue paper. 8⅟₁₆ × 7 inches (20.5 × 17.8 cm.). Lightly stained. Lined.

Once the task of assembling Sassoferrato's painted portraits is undertaken, it is likely that the substantial Roman lady who is the subject of this typical squared drawing will be identified without too much difficulty. Marked by her headdress as a widow, she may possibly have been an owner of one of the devotional pictures that Sassoferrato produced in such large numbers, almost exclusively for private patrons. The subject, obviously studied from life, was apparently intended to fit into an oval format.

Beyond the sixty sheets by the artist at Windsor Castle, the artist's drawings seem to be of some rarity and occur only occasionally in major collections.

PROVENANCE: Sir Thomas Lawrence (Lugt 2445); Charles Fairfax Murray; purchased by J. Pierpont Morgan in London, 1910.

BIBLIOGRAPHY: Fairfax Murray, I, no. 27, repr.

The Pierpont Morgan Library
No. I, 27

Stefano della Bella

Florence 1610–Florence 1664

87 *Pages in the Cavalcade of the Polish Ambassador on His Entrance into Rome, 1633*

Pen and brown ink, over preliminary drawing in lead or graphite pencil. 6³⁄₁₆ × 17⅜ inches (15.7 × 44.1 cm.). Yellow and brown stains; vertical fold line at center; repaired loss of upper right corner. Watermark: bird on a heraldic mountain composed of three hills. Lined.

Inscribed in pencil in a modern hand at lower right margin, *Stefano della Bella*; showing through from verso in an older hand in pen and brown ink at upper center, *Stefano della Bella*; another short, illegible inscription at a right angle to the other.

Among the young Stefano's first projects on his arrival in Rome from Florence was the execution of a panoramic etching recording the ceremonial entrance of another visitor, the Polish Ambassador George Ossolinsky who rode into the city with his colorful cortège on Sunday, November 27, 1633. The print, which is dedicated to Lorenzo de' Medici (1599–1648) who sponsored Stefano's Roman trip, is composed of six segments, each accompanied by an explanatory inscription (De Vesme 44–49).

The Morgan drawing is a preparatory study for the section of the etching lettered I and K, representing "Venti paggi di S. E. vestiti di colori d'acqua marina e fondo ranciato" and, at the far right, two of five Turkish horses decked with heron feathers and jewels. The drawing shows the twenty pages, but in a slightly different arrangement from those of the print. The fifth horseman from the left was suppressed in the print and another added in the gap between the twelfth and thirteenth horsemen of the drawing. The ornamental patterns of the saddle cloths have not yet been indicated, but otherwise drawing and print are virtually identical. The two Turkish horses were etched without alteration.

The Morgan drawing is executed in the same direction as the etching, as seems to be true of certain other drawings related to the print. Matthias Winner (in the catalogue of the exhibition "Entwurf und Ausführung," Berlin, Kupferstichkabinett, 1964, no. 7) cites the sketch from the Pacetti collection in the Berlin Kupferstichkabinett (no. 15702) as a study for the horses of Section K. The rather dry Louvre drawing Inv. 434, which relates to the subject of Section G, may be a copy.

Count Seilern's *Four Polish Riders* (repr. *Italian Paintings and Drawings at 56 Princes Gate London*, London, 1959, pl. 76) and a rather freer sketch in the Uffizi (Inv. 6003) of three mounted archers do not appear to have been directly utilized for the 1633 print. There are a number of sketches of Polish subjects in the dismembered sketchbook in the Albertina, probably the raw materials the artist used in developing the lengthy composition of the procession. The 1775 sale catalogue of Pierre-Jean Mariette, a great fancier of Stefano, mentions a drawing (no. 184) representing the entrance of the Polish Ambassador into Rome, "dessin capital & d'une parfaite conservation," that is now in the Louvre (Inv. 430); others relating to the ambitious print may have perished in the fire that destroyed most of the collection of André-Charles Boulle in 1720.

In 1645, Stefano, then in France, recorded the entrance of another Polish ambassador, but this time into Paris, in a series of fourteen drawings, apparently never etched, and now in the British Museum (1895.6.17.387/400).

PROVENANCE: Sir John Charles Robinson (Lugt 1433); Charles Fairfax Murray; purchased by J. Pierpont Morgan in London, 1910.

The Pierpont Morgan Library
No. IV, 179b

24 cm.). Repaired loss at lower margin center; small loss at left margin center; fold line across upper half. Lined.

Inscribed on verso of lining in pencil and pen and brown ink with various numbers and notations.

The drawing contains the main motif of Stefano's etching of a deer hunt, one of a series of nine prints devoted to the hunting of ostrich, wild boar, and deer (De Vesme 732–740). In the etching De Vesme 739, which is in the opposite direction, the artist added a second horseman in the middle distance at the point in the present drawing where there is a slight notation of a second deer; he also enhanced the huntsman's chances by depicting two does running ahead of the stag and supplying a couple of dogs. Stefano apparently began his drawing in graphite with the sheet turned in the opposite direction, then turned the paper around and started again.

A drawing in the Uffizi (Inv. 434), in the same direction as the etching, shows the artist studying the positions of the hunter's hand grasping the spear and that holding the reins, passages that he glosses over in the Morgan drawing. The Uffizi also has a number of other drawings that are preparatory for the hunt series (Inv. 868 o for De Vesme 732; 8027 for De Vesme 733; 870 o, 896 o for De Vesme 734; 7967 for De Vesme 738); another sheet of studies in the Morgan Library (no. IV, 179a), which has the same provenance as the present one, is preparatory for De Vesme 740, and has a variant sketch for De Vesme 733. Still other studies for hunts are in the Albertina (Inv. 532 for De Vesme 733; Inv. 533 for De Vesme 737). Robert and Bertina Suida Manning own a sketch for a wolf hunt.

PROVENANCE: Thomas Dimsdale (Lugt 2426); A. Donnadieu (Lugt 725); Dr. Barry Delany (Lugt 350); Charles Fairfax Murray; purchased by J. Pierpont Morgan in London, 1910.

BIBLIOGRAPHY: Fairfax Murray, IV, no. 179, repr.

The Pierpont Morgan Library
No. IV, 179

88 *Stag Hunt*

Pen and brown ink, graphite. The pinkness of the sheet is due to its having been rubbed with red chalk on the verso, probably in anticipation of tracing. 5¼ × 9⁷⁄₁₆ inches (13.3 ×

89 *Two Women and Their Dogs Watching Deer*

Pen and brown ink, brown wash, over black chalk. 5⅛ × 9⅜ inches (12.9 × 23.8 cm.). Lined.

Although in subject and format this sheet would seem to be related to the series of hunts designed and etched by Stefano, the composition does not appear among his known prints as far as can be determined. The barefoot girls checking the two mastiffs intent upon the running deer were possibly intended as nymphs rather than as participants in an ordinary hunting scene like that of No. 88. The etching De Vesme 208, which shows a similar (but differently posed) figure, holding a straining dog by the collar and identified as a huntress by the quiver at her side, is variously described as "Une nymphe" or "La belle chasseresse"; a drawing in the Uffizi (Inv. 7986) relates to this print (see O. H. Giglioli, "Mostra degli incisori toscani del Seicento," Florence, Società Leonardo da Vinci, 1942, under no. 181). It is a commentary on Stefano's working habits that the girl and dog at the right repeat the pose and stance, although in the reverse, of the pikeman and dog of the deer hunt represented in De Vesme 738.

The drawing is an attractive example of the soft manner of the artist's later period. It combines the *sfumato* of the wash with a delicate but energetic line in an effect that is entirely different from the brisk regularity of the Callot-like technique of Stefano's early style, so well exemplified by No. 87 of the exhibition.

Private Collection

90 *Nude Man Pounding*

Red chalk. 8½ × 7¾ inches (21.5 × 19.7 cm.). Irregularly shaped hole at center; staining at margins; horizontal crease across lower quarter. Lined.

Inscribed in pen and brown ink at upper left, *S. D. B.*

An academy drawing in red chalk is unusual in Stefano's work, but this study from the nude, despite the difference in medium, may be effectively compared with the studies in pen and brown ink over black chalk at Oxford, Vienna, and Windsor. As J. Byam Shaw has remarked, even the model appears to be the same in the Oxford and Manning drawings (for the former, see Parker, *Ashmolean Catalogue*, II, no. 786, repr.). Blunt describes the

Windsor sheets as "life studies in classical poses" (*Castiglione and Della Bella at Windsor*, nos. 82, 83 [neither repr.]), noting the possibility that Windsor no. 82, which is somewhat inferior, may be by Livio Mehus, the young Fleming who was Stefano's pupil and companion on his journey to Rome around 1651; the superior quality of the Manning sheet, which is worked with the utmost delicacy and surety, rules out any such authorship.

Since it is clearly a mature work, the drawing may have been done at the time Stefano was instructing young Cosimo III de' Medici in drawing, about 1657. Byam Shaw, in correspondence, refers to the Manning and Oxford sheets as "fairly late drawings, in his best style, after, or not long before, his return from France to Italy." De Vesme placed the etchings nos. 484 and 485, described as "Académie de jeune homme gaignant les mains" and "Académie de jeune homme assis par terre," at about 1662. The Manning drawing should also be considered in the context of the Windsor study of a faun (Blunt, no. 105) and that of a male nude, apparently a model holding onto a rope, in the collection of Sir Anthony Blunt (London, Courtauld Institute of Art, "Sir Anthony Blunt Collection," 1964, no. 16).

Robert and Bertina Suida Manning

91 *Design for a Monstrance*

Pen and brown ink, gray wash, over black chalk. 15⅜ × 9½ inches (39.1 × 24.1 cm.). Upper corners rounded; one vertical and two horizontal creases. Lined.

Della Bella, a gifted decorator, made a number of sketches for ornamental metalwork. This design for a monstrance is unusually large and complete. At Windsor there is a less finished pen study for a similar monstrance, supported by three angels with upraised arms (Blunt, *Castiglione and Della Bella at Windsor*, p. 95, no. 44), and in the Spencer collection, from which this drawing comes, there was another "elegant and rich design for the Porte Dieu." The Uffizi possesses a series of smaller designs for oil lamps, and there were many ornament drawings in an album of Stefano's sketches formerly in the collection of Sir George Holford, sold at Sotheby's, March 22, 1928, no. 29B.

PROVENANCE: The Earls Spencer (Lugt 1530); Spencer sale, London, June 10, 1811, no. 236 or no. 237; Dr. Barry Delany (Lugt 350); purchased by the Metropolitan Museum in London, 1961.

BIBLIOGRAPHY: Bean, *100 European Drawings*, no. 35, repr.

The Metropolitan Museum of Art
Rogers Fund, 61.131.1

Giovanni Francesco Romanelli

Viterbo about 1610–Viterbo 1662

92 *The Construction and Restoration of Churches under Countess Matilda*

Pen and brown ink, brown wash, with traces of graphite. 7⁵⁄₁₆ × 7¹⁵⁄₁₆ inches (18.6 × 20.2 cm.).

Inscribed on verso in pen and brown ink in an old hand, *La Contessa Matilda fabricò diverse chiese e molte ne | ristaurò tutti gli autori lo affermano che di lei anno scritt[o]*; in another hand, *yo*; at lower left, *n | 24*.

As Cardinal Maffeo Barberini, Pope Urban VIII had expressed his veneration for Matilda, Countess of Tuscany (1046–1115), in poetic form. As pontiff, he had the body of the great eleventh-century benefactress of the Church removed from Mantua to Rome, where, in St. Peter's on March 20, 1637, Bernini's new tomb for the countess was unveiled. In the same year, Romanelli began work on the Pope's commission for a series of frescoes illustrating the life of the countess in a room on an upper floor of the Vatican Palace. Known as the Sala della Contessa Matilda, the room is used for the housing of liturgical vestments and is generally inaccessible to the public. The present drawing and its companion (No. 93) are two of Romanelli's designs for the frescoes, which he completed five years later in 1642. Strongly under the influence of the style of Romanelli's master, Pietro da Cortona, the two sheets passed under his name for many years until they were recognized as Romanelli's studies for the Matilda series by Sir Anthony Blunt and Walter Vitzthum.

The fresco for which this drawing is preparatory is the southernmost of the two central panels of the vault of the Sala della Contessa Matilda; the other represents the donations of the countess to the Cathedral of Parma. The fresco follows the composition of the drawing with only minor alterations, the most obvious being the elimination of the small figures of the two workmen in the background at the left. Jakob Hess in his informative article in *L'Illustrazione Vaticana*, VI, 1935, no. 5, pp. 241–245, thought that the façade and campanile in the background of the fresco were close enough to the aspect of the cathedral at Modena to identify the scene as taking place there, and he titled the fresco *The Construction of the Cathedral of Modena*, obviously assuming that the cathedral seen completed in the distance is under construction in the foreground.

PROVENANCE: Marquis de Lagoy (Lugt 1710); William Esdaile (Lugt 2617); Sir John Charles Robinson (Lugt 1433); Charles Fairfax Murray; purchased by J. Pierpont Morgan in London, 1910.

The Pierpont Morgan Library
No. IV, 173b

93 *Countess Matilda Giving Shelter to Bishop Anselm*

Pen and brown ink, brown wash, squared in graphite. 7⁵⁄₁₆ × 6¹⁄₁₆ inches (18.5 × 15.4 cm.). Watermark: fleur-de-lis in a circle (probably Heawood 1610).

Inscribed on verso in pen and brown ink in an old hand, partially cut, *Si ricoverano dalla Contessa Matilda molti sacer . . . | e vescovi et fra li altri Anselmo Vescovo . . . | che fugiono dalla Citta di Roma da' Arrigo Impe | Autori il Sigonio et il biondo et altri. . . .*

As the old inscription on the back of the drawing indicates, it represents the countess receiving Bishop Anselm of Lucca, her confessor and advisor, and the other priests and bishops who were fleeing from the Emperor Henry IV. Although this subject is not among those mentioned or illustrated by Jakob Hess in *L'Illustrazione Vaticana*, VI, 1935, D. Redig de Campos of the Vatican writes that the corresponding fresco is the first to the west on the north side of the vault of the Sala Matilda in the Vatican. Romanelli's dependence on Cortona is pointed up in a detail like the gesture of the countess, which is an adaptation of the attitude of the

Queen of Sheba in Cortona's early painting in the Palazzo Mattei (cf. No. 53 of the exhibition). According to Walter Vitzthum, there is another drawing relating to the frescoes of the Sala della Contessa Matilda in the Gabinetto Nazionale delle Stampe, Rome.

Apropos of the great medieval personality who is the subject of what is perhaps Romanelli's most pleasing work, it might be added that the Morgan Library's illuminated manuscript *The Gospels of Matilda, Countess of Tuscany* (M. 492), which came from S. Benedetto di Polirone, was originally the gift of the "Gran Contessa" to that monastery which enjoyed her special favor.

PROVENANCE: Charles Fairfax Murray; purchased by J. Pierpont Morgan in London, 1910.

The Pierpont Morgan Library
No. IV, 173a

94 *Justice and Abundance*

Watercolor, chiefly in blues, reds, and browns, over black chalk. $4\frac{5}{8} \times 7\frac{7}{8}$ inches (11.7 × 20 cm.). The lunette has been silhouetted and laid down on a sheet of blue paper measuring $4\frac{11}{16} \times 8$ inches (11.9 × 20.4 cm.). Some breaks and losses in upper half. Insert by artist in area of Abundance's arm to alter position of hand.

On his second visit to France (1655–1657), Romanelli was employed by Anne of Austria, the Queen Mother, in the decoration of her apartment in the Palais du Louvre, the rooms that are now known as the Salles des Saisons, de la Paix, de Sévère, and des Antonins. On the ceiling of the Salle des Antonins, then the queen's bedroom, he painted amid the stuccoed ornamentation by Girardon a composition of Religion accompanied by Faith, Hope, and Charity; at the ends of the room, the stories of Esther and Judith; and in the lunettes, various combinations of Virtues. This drawing and the following (No. 95), finished in the bright watercolor tints the artist favored in his Parisian period, are studies—quite possibly models for the perusal of the royal patron—for two of Romanelli's four lunette frescoes. (Actually, there are six lunettes in all, but two are later, the work of Lethière [1760–1832]. The fact that these two are those on the wall along the Seine suggests that they may be replacements for paintings by Romanelli that were destroyed by dampness). The frescoes of *Justice and Abundance* and *Prudence and Foresight*, which face each other across the center of the chamber, are in the same direction as the Manning drawings and follow them faithfully. Jacob Bean points out that four related drawings in Stockholm (nos. 544–548) are Romanelli's designs for the putti occupying the painted circular openings above each lunette.

The titles used in the present catalogue are those employed by De Clarac in his description of the frescoes, which he speaks of as being in questionable condition at the time (*Musée de sculpture antique et moderne ou description historique et graphique du Louvre . . .*, I, Paris, 1841 ed., p. 534). He describes Justice as holding a rule and sword, and leaning on the codex of the law; Abundance's cornucopia and olive branch indicate that she owes her riches to peace. The subjects of Romanelli's other existing lunettes are *Temperance and Peace* and *Continence*.

PROVENANCE: M. de Bourguignon de Fabregoules (see Lugt 1015); Charles-Joseph-Barthélmi Giraud (according to Chennevières sale catalogue; see also Lugt 1015); M. Flury-Hérard (Lugt 1015); Flury-Hérard sale, Paris, Blaisot, May 13–15, 1861, no. 327; Marquis Philippe de Chennevières (Lugt 2072); Chennevières sale, Paris, P. Roblin, April 4–7, 1900, no. 452.

BIBLIOGRAPHY: Walter Vitzthum, review of Detroit exhibition, *Master Drawings*, III, no. 4, 1965, p. 407.

EXHIBITIONS: Detroit, Italy 1600–1700, 1965, no. 38, repr.

Robert and Bertina Suida Manning

95 *Prudence and Foresight*

Watercolor, chiefly in blues, reds, and browns, over black and red chalk. $4\frac{9}{16} \times 7\frac{5}{8}$ inches (11.7 × 19.5 cm.). The lunette has been silhouetted and laid down on a sheet of blue paper measuring $4\frac{5}{8} \times 8$ inches (11.8 × 20.2 cm.). Repaired losses at lower margin and lower right corner; small loss on left arm of Foresight; other small breaks.

According to De Clarac (see No. 94 above), Foresight is shown presenting a mirror to Prudence, who is identified by the serpent in her hand. The lamp is a reminder to both that they must be unceasingly watchful.

PROVENANCE: See No. 94 above.

Robert and Bertina Suida Manning

Giulio Carpioni

Venice 1611–Venice 1674

96 *Studies for a Composition of Bacchus and Ariadne*

Red chalk. 7½ × 7¹⁵⁄₁₆ inches (19 × 20.1 cm.). Repaired loss, upper left corner. Watermark: crawfish in a circle.

Fairfax Murray acquired this sheet as one of a lot of nine drawings from the collection of Sir Henry Hawley, sold at Christie's on July 16, 1891, as "the property of a Baronet." Only a figure study by Bassano was identified in the auction catalogue's description of the lot, but in the notes that Fairfax Murray made for his own records (now preserved at the University of Texas, Austin), he described the present drawing and lists it as "Carpioni." Whether this was his own identification or a reflection of a traditional ascription, the attribution is reinforced by the correspondence between the male figure of the drawing and the Bacchus in the painting *Bacchus and Ariadne* in the collection of Vittor Luigi Braga, Vicenza (Giuseppe Maria Pilo, *Carpioni*, Venice [1961], pl. 58). The reclining female figure was no doubt intended as Ariadne although she does not appear in the Braga picture. She could also have taken her place amid the languid company of sleepers and dreamers in Carpioni's numerous representations of the realm of Hypnos.

Whereas the artist seems to have settled immediately on the position of the female figure, the several trial sketches of the Bacchus reveal his energetic exploration of possibilities of gesture and stance, although he never obscures the source of his ultimate inspiration in Titian's great god.

PROVENANCE: Sir Joseph Hawley (according to the Fairfax Murray Notebooks); [Sir Henry Hawley] sale, London, Christie's, July 16, 1891, part of no. 211; Charles Fairfax Murray; purchased by J. Pierpont Morgan in London, 1910.

BIBLIOGRAPHY: Fairfax Murray, IV, no. 86, repr.

The Pierpont Morgan Library
No. IV, 86

Baldassare Franceschini, called il Volterrano

Volterra 1611–Florence 1689

97 *Allegory in Honor of Vittoria della Rovere*

Red chalk and red wash. 13⁵⁄₁₆ × 8⅝ inches (33.9 × 21.9 cm.). Stain at upper left corner. Lined.

Numbered on verso in pen and black ink, *63*. Collector's mark of Janos Scholz at lower left (Lugt S. 2933b).

For Vittoria della Rovere, wife of Ferdinando II de' Medici, Grand Duke of Tuscany, Volterrano decorated a room in the Palazzo Pitti, filling the five sections of the ceiling with allegorical allusions to her name and merits. This drawing is the painter's study for the central section of the decoration. Baldinucci supplies a brief iconographic description of this section, pointing out "Victory with palm branches and a garland of laurel in her hands. There is also Fortitude who has an oak tree [*rovere* in Italian] in her arms, above which passes a banderole on which is written *Arbore Victoria*. Below this stupendous figure are many arms of war, and also Fame sounding her trumpet." (Baldinucci, *Notizie*, XVII, p. 107). The Uffizi possesses a study for another section of the ceiling, where Peace is represented setting fire to military equipment (3262 Santarelli). Vittoria della Rovere married her cousin Ferdinando in 1634 at the age of fourteen, and the event is alluded to symbolically in Pietro da Cortona's frescoes in the Camera della Stufa of the Palazzo Pitti (see No. 60), which date from at least a decade earlier than Volterrano's decorations in the Pitti. The latter are strongly influenced by Cortona's example, which was the major force in Tuscan painting of the seventeenth century.

EXHIBITIONS: Scholz Exhibitions: Oakland, 1961, no. 37; Columbia, S.C., 1961, no. 39; Hamburg, 1963, no. 61, pl. 30; New Haven, 1964, no. 61.

Janos Scholz

Simone Cantarini

Oropezza (near Pesaro) 1612–Verona 1648

98 *Studies of an Infant in Various Poses*

Red chalk. 10³⁄₁₆ × 8¹⁄₁₆ inches (25.8 × 20.4 cm.). Small repaired losses at corners. Watermark: bird on a heraldic mountain composed of three hills (resembles Heawood 161).

Cantarini's grace as a draughtsman is well illustrated in this sympathetic and observant portrayal of infancy. These red chalk sketches of a lively baby, done from life, seem to have been made with the possibility of further utilization. In the sketch at the lower left showing an infant figure with upraised right hand and crossed ankles, seated on the lap of a draped personage, the artist is no longer directly engaged by his cherubic sitter but is thinking in terms of the hieratic pose of the Blessing Christ Child as it might be presented in a painting.

PROVENANCE: Sir Charles Greville (Lugt 549); Earls of Warwick (Lugt 2600); purchased by the Morgan Library in London, 1963.

BIBLIOGRAPHY: Morgan Library, *Thirteenth Fellows Report, 1963–1964*, pp. 98-99.

EXHIBITIONS: London, Alpine Club Gallery, "Old Master Drawings Presented by W. R. Jeudwine," 1962, no. 7; Vancouver Art Gallery, "The Nude in Art," 1964, no. 44.

The Pierpont Morgan Library
Gift of the Fellows, 1963.4

Pier Francesco Mola

Coldrerio (Como) 1612–Rome 1666

99 *St. John the Baptist Preaching*

Pen and brown ink, brown and red wash, red chalk. 7⅞ × 10¾ inches (20 × 27.4 cm.). Vertical crease at center; spot of blue oil paint at left. Lined.

The Baptist Preaching was a favorite subject with Mola, one that enabled him to introduce a landscape background in the Bolognese taste and genre details, like the boatman in the right middle ground, derived from Annibale Carracci. A number of painted versions of this subject exist; they are all distinguished by inventive variations in composition, as are drawings of the subject in the École des Beaux-Arts, Paris, the Louvre (Inv. 8405, 8406, and 14,160, the latter as anonymous Italian), the Ashmolean Museum (Parker, *Ashmolean Catalogue*, II, no. 909), and at Holkham Hall.

PROVENANCE: J. A. Gere, London.

Donald P. Gurney

100 *A Cleric Dictating His Last Will and Testament*

Pen and brown ink, brown wash, over black chalk. 10 × 15⅜ inches (25.4 × 39.1 cm.). Vertical crease at center. Watermark: six-pointed star, *S* at center, within a circle, cross at top. Lined.

Numbered in pen and brown ink at lower right, *38*.

Mola, who studied in Bologna, was quick to follow the local fashion for savage and sometimes scabrous caricature. He produced many such a comic scene, full of witty and occasionally recondite allusions, and he was prone to choose scholars, critics, and ecclesiastics as the butts of his satire. As a caricaturist, Mola owes a particular debt to Guercino.

EXHIBITIONS: Hamburg, Scholz Exhibition, 1963, no. 95, pl. 61.

Janos Scholz

101 *The Impoverished Artist*

Red chalk. 11⅜ × 7⅝ inches (28.9 × 19.4 cm.). Watermark: bird on a heraldic mountain composed of three hills.

Inscribed in pencil in a late hand at lower left, *Mola*; numbered in pen and brown ink at lower right, *99*.

As in various other drawings, notably at Oxford, it is possibly Mola himself who is caricatured here. He depicts a rudely gesturing artist who has sprouted wings and apparently gone on to higher things, leaving behind such mundane obligations as his wine bills. The wine seller flourishes an unpaid tab, undoubtedly companion to those tucked in the opening of the artist's coat. The scene would appear to illustrate the painter's wishful thought that when confronted by his wine bills, he might drop his palette and brush, and ascend on a cloud, leaving the importunate vendor in the path of a bolt of lightning. Red chalk is an unusual medium for Mola's caricatures, but his style is unmistakable here.

PROVENANCE: Purchased by the Morgan Library in London, 1965.

BIBLIOGRAPHY: Morgan Library, *Fourteenth Fellows Report, 1965–1966*, p. 119.

The Pierpont Morgan Library
Gift of the Fellows, 1965.8

102 *The Conversion of St. Paul*

Pen and brown ink, brown wash, over black chalk. 8⅝ × 10¹⁵⁄₁₆ inches (22 × 27.8 cm.). Left margin irregular. Watermark: fleur-de-lis in a circle.

Numbered in black chalk at lower margin, *27 16*.

Dramatic use of very dark wash and nervous, abbreviated contour lines suggests that this is a drawing of Mola's maturity. In style it is close to the artist's preparatory studies for the 1656–1657 fresco in the Quirinal Palace representing Joseph Recognized by His Brethren. The Conversion of St. Paul is the subject of one of the two frescoes painted by Mola at an uncertain date in the Ravenna Chapel of the Gesù in Rome. There the composition differs in a great many ways from the present drawing, but the possibility of a connection between the fresco and the drawing should not be dismissed. The latter is related in style to a recently published sheet, certainly a study for Mola's other fresco in the Ravenna Chapel, representing St. Peter Baptizing the Centurion in Prison (the drawing repr. by John Rowlands in *Master Drawings*, II, no. 3, 1964, pl. 22). The Ravenna Chapel frescoes have sometimes been assigned an early date, but Ann B. Sutherland (*Burlington Magazine*, CVI, 1964, p. 367) has established that they had not been painted by 1639. Passeri discusses the Gesù frescoes after Mola's work in the Quirinal in 1656–1657, and the style of the drawing published by Rowlands and of the present sheet, assuming that it is a study for the Gesù, would accord well with this relatively late date in Mola's career.

Mrs. Richard Krautheimer

Domenico Gargiulo, called Micco Spadaro

Naples 1612–Naples 1675

103 *Man Standing by a Rearing Horse, and Other Studies*

Pen and brown ink. 7½ × 9¹⁵⁄₁₆ inches (19 × 25.3 cm.). Upper corners replaced. Watermark: donkey (?) within a circle.

Inscribed in pen and brown ink at lower left, *No. 26* (?); at lower right, *Spadaro*.

The traditional attribution of this spirited sketch to the relatively little-known Micco Spadaro is confirmed by comparison on the one hand with figures that animate the artist's landscapes, and on the other with a group of drawings, also traditionally given to Micco Spadaro, that figured in the collection of Don Pedro de Bórbon, Duque de Dúrcal. The Duke of Dúrcal's drawings, predominantly Neapolitan, were sold at auction in New York in 1889, and most of those ascribed to Micco Spadaro passed eventually to the Metropolitan Museum and to the National Collection of Fine Arts in Washington. In the Dúrcal group one encounters the vivacious, scratchy pen work that characterizes the present sketch, and the same lively hand is recognizable in drawings in Berlin and at the Louvre. A group of pen sketches in the Cooper Union has been attributed to Micco Spadaro on the basis of an inscription, *M. sp. fe*, that appears on one of the drawings; these studies of popular types may represent another aspect of his pen draughtsmanship, although they are much less assured and incisive than the present drawing (for the Cooper Union group see the exhibition catalogue, Sarasota, The Ringling Museums, "Baroque Painters of Naples," 1961, nos. 53–57).

PROVENANCE: Giovanni Piancastelli (no mark, see Lugt S. 2078a); Mr. and Mrs. Edward Brandegee (no mark, see Lugt S. 1860c).

BIBLIOGRAPHY: Walter Vitzthum, "Neapolitan Seicento Drawings in Florida," *Burlington Magazine*, CIII, 1961, p. 314, fig. 24; Walter Vitzthum, "Le Dessin baroque à Naples," *L'Oeil*, no. 97, 1963, repr. p. 50.

Janos Scholz

Mattia Preti

Taverna (Calabria) 1613–Malta 1699

104 *Flying Figure Appearing before an Enthroned Figure*

Red chalk. 8 × 12³⁄₁₆ inches (20.4 × 31 cm.). Lined.

Inscribed in pen and brown ink at lower right, *P. M.*; illegible inscription in pencil along lower margin; unidentified paraph in pen and brown ink at lower left.

In abbreviated strokes of red chalk Preti here suggests light and movement with great authority.

The drawing may be a study for a section of a ceiling fresco, given the steep perspective in which the figures are seen. The brevity of Preti's highly personal style looks back to the drawings of Lanfranco and forward to those of Luca Giordano.

PROVENANCE: Purchased by the Metropolitan Museum in London, 1965.

EXHIBITIONS: London, Alpine Club Gallery, "Old Master Drawings Presented by Yvonne ffrench," 1965, no. 16.

The Metropolitan Museum of Art
Rogers Fund, 65.111.2

Salvator Rosa

Naples 1615–Rome 1673

105 *Witches' Sabbath*

Pen and brown ink, pale brown and a little gray wash. 10 11/16 × 7 1/4 inches (27.2 × 18.4 cm.).

In overall composition and in many important details this drawing is related to a picture in the Corsini collection in Florence representing witches armed with cabalistic symbols conjuring from a fire a ghostly skeleton and a fire-breathing dragon. Baldinucci records this commission, which probably dates from the 1640s: "Al Marchese Bartolommeo Corsini dipinse un bel quadro d'incantesimi e stregonerie" (*Notizie*, XIX, p. 28). A sheet in the Uffizi (12,102 F) and three at Princeton (one repr. *Italian Drawings in The Art Museum, Princeton University*, Princeton, 1966, no. 56) bear rapid pen sketches related to figures in the present drawing and in the Corsini picture.

PROVENANCE: Sir Charles Greville (Lugt 549); Earls of Warwick (Lugt 2600); J. P. Richter, London; purchased by the Metropolitan Museum in London, 1912.

BIBLIOGRAPHY: Hans Tietze, *European Master Drawings in the United States*, New York, 1947, p. 160, no. 80, repr.; Walter Vitzthum, "Le Dessin baroque à Naples," *L'Oeil*, no. 97, 1963, repr. p. 50; Luigi Salerno, *Salvator Rosa*, Milan, 1963, p. 63; Bean, *100 European Drawings*, no. 36, repr.

The Metropolitan Museum of Art
Rogers Fund, 12.56.13

106 *The Prodigal Son Kneeling Repentant among Swine*

Pen and brown ink, brown wash, on brownish paper.

15 3/16 × 10 15/16 inches (38.5 × 27.8 cm.). Spot of brown wash at upper left corner. Lined.

Drawing fixed to a Mariette mount inscribed, *SALVATOR ROSA NE . . . L . . .*; inscribed on verso of mount in pen and brown ink, *R Willett's coll^n 1808 WE*; *Formerly in the coll of Mariette. at M Mariette's Sale cost 450 francs.*

This large drawing may well have been made in preparation for Rosa's picture representing the Prodigal Son as a swineherd. In the picture, now in the Hermitage (repr. Salerno, pl. 37), the Prodigal kneels facing left before a clump of trees that rises to the right, as here, but the troupe under his care includes goats, sheep, and a cow as well as the swine described in the biblical parable. Rosa no doubt increased the number and variety of animals in order to display his skill as an animal painter. The picture, which is datable in the late 1650s, passed to the Hermitage from the Walpole collection at Houghton Hall. Horace Walpole singled it out in his description of the pictures at Houghton: "In Lord Orford's Prodigal is represented the extremity of Misery and low Nature; not foul and burlesque like Michael Angelo Caravaggio; not minute, circumstantial and laborious like the Dutch Painters." (*Aedes Walpolianae*, London, 1752, p. XXVII).

In style and in dimensions the drawing is very close to two sheets in the British Museum representing single figures silhouetted against great twisted trees (P.p. 5–105 and P.p. 5–107). When the drawing was in William Esdaile's collection it was reproduced in reverse with a few variations in a chiaroscuro woodcut by John Skippe dated 1809. Previously the drawing had figured in the collection of Pierre-Jean Mariette. In Basan's catalogue of the Mariette sale it is described as ". . . fait avec tout l'art possible; le Paysage y est traité de la plus grande manière, et la lumière très bien distribuée," and at the sale it fetched a high price— 450 *livres*—that reflected French eighteenth-century taste for Rosa's picturesque landscapes with figures. An old copy of the drawing is at Princeton (62.64, as Sebastiano Ricci).

PROVENANCE: Pierre-Jean Mariette (Lugt 1852); Mariette sale, Paris, 1775–1776, no. 666; R. Willett (according to inscription on verso of mount); William Esdaile (Lugt 2617); Alfred A. de Pass (Lugt S. 108a); presented by him to the Royal Institution of Cornwall, Truro (Lugt S.

2014e); sale, London, Christie's, November 30, 1965, no. 192, repr., bought by the Metropolitan Museum.

BIBLIOGRAPHY: George Penrose, *Royal Institution of Cornwall. Cornwall County Museum and Art Gallery. Truro. Catalogue of Paintings, Drawings and Miniatures in the Alfred A. de Pass Collection*, Truro, 1936, p. 23, no. 198; Luigi Salerno, *Salvator Rosa*, Milan, 1963, p. 37.

EXHIBITIONS: London, Arts Council, "Drawings from the Alfred A. de Pass Collection," 1957, no. 17; London, Royal Academy of Arts, "Primitives to Picasso," 1962, no. 323.

The Metropolitan Museum of Art
Rogers Fund, 66.1

107 *St. Philip Baptizing the Eunuch*

Pen and brown ink, brown wash, touches of gray wash. $6\frac{5}{16} \times 4\frac{7}{16}$ inches (16.1 × 11.3 cm.).

Numbered on verso in pencil at upper right, *14 / M8*.

Verso: Partially cut pen and brown ink study of a head and raised arm.

As was first observed by Walter Vitzthum, this vigorous drawing is a study for the central group of Rosa's painting *St. Philip Baptizing the Eunuch*, a work of the artist's mature years, which, with its companion piece *St. John Preaching in the Wilderness*, is now in the Chrysler Collection in Provincetown, Massachusetts. The pair, remarkably enough, have never been separated since they were executed for Monsignore Giovanni Battista Costaguti (died 1704), about 1660 in the opinion of Luigi Salerno (*Salvator Rosa*, Milan, 1963, p. 50). The group of St. Philip and the Eunuch as it finally appears in the painting shows that the artist's ideas were still at a fluid stage when the Morgan drawing was set down with slashing pen and bold washes. While the Eunuch's pose remains substantially the same in the painting, the figure faces in the opposite direction. The figure of St. Philip is completely detached so that it is silhouetted in its entirety; the arm holding the baptismal basin is lowered, and the other, which clasps his garments in the drawing, is raised to point heavenward. These effective changes served to make the Eunuch's head and the baptismal bowl just above it the focal point of the composition. Michael Mahoney, who is preparing a monograph

on Rosa's drawings, has discovered two other preparatory studies for the painting in European collections, one of which is an early idea for the saint baptizing. On the basis of the style of the drawings for both the *St. Philip* and its pendant, Mr. Mahoney dates the Chrysler paintings in the late 1650s, about 1659.

The story of the baptism of the "man of Ethiopia, a eunuch of great authority under Candace, queen of the Ethiopians" is told in Acts 8:26–39.

PROVENANCE: Amédée-Paul-Émile Gasc (Lugt 1131); Charles Fairfax Murray; purchased by J. Pierpont Morgan in London, 1910.

BIBLIOGRAPHY: Walter Vitzthum, "Neapolitan Seicento Drawings in Florida," *Burlington Magazine*, CIII, 1961, p. 314; *Art in Italy, 1600–1700* (exhibition catalogue), Detroit, Institute of Arts, 1965, under nos. 155, 156.

The Pierpont Morgan Library
No. I, 108a

108 *The Fall of the Giants*

Pen and brown ink, over black chalk. $10\frac{5}{16} \times 7\frac{13}{16}$ inches (26.2 × 19.8 cm.). Lined.

Preparatory study for Rosa's etching, the *Fall of the Giants* (Bartsch, XX, p. 276, no. 21), a work described as already finished in a letter from the artist to his friend G. B. Ricciardi dated July 14, 1663 (A. de Rinaldis, *Lettere inedite di Salvator Rosa a G. B. Ricciardi*, Rome, 1939, p. 153). In the etched design, which is more than twice as large as this drawing, the dramatic diagonal composition is essentially the same, but the wrathful figure of Jove appears at the top of the composition. Rosa's representation of the primeval cataclysm was perhaps inspired by Giulio Romano's frescoes in the Sala dei Giganti of the Palazzo del Te in Mantua, painted more than a century earlier, but his composition is nonetheless entirely original. The angularity and brevity of Rosa's late style is apparent when this study is compared with other earlier drawings by the artist in the present exhibition. Michael Mahoney has identified further studies by Rosa for the *Fall of the Giants* in Leipzig, Edinburgh, and the Farnesina in Rome.

PROVENANCE: Purchased by the Metropolitan Museum in London, 1964.

The Metropolitan Museum of Art
Rogers Fund, 64.197.6

Bernardo Cavallino

Naples 1616–Naples 1654

109 *The Virgin Immaculate*

Black chalk on gray-green paper. 14 15/16 × 10 11/16 inches (37.9 × 27.2 cm.). Horizontal crease at center; several brown stains.

Inscribed in pen and brown ink at lower left, *Bernardo Cavallino.*

Study for an *Immacolata* formerly in a private collection in Palermo (repr. *L'Arte,* XXIII, 1920, p. 267), as Oreste Ferrari has pointed out. Drawings by Cavallino, one of the most graceful and engaging painters in seventeenth-century Naples, are exceedingly rare. Vitzthum mentions two traditionally and plausibly attributed sheets in Naples, and the Ashmolean Museum at Oxford possesses a chalk study for a St. Sebastian, very similar in facial type and notation to the present example (repr. Parker, *Ashmolean Catalogue,* II, no. 816, pl. CLXXVII). The Oxford sheet is inscribed *Bernardo Cavallino* in the same hand that marked the attribution on this drawing. Judging from these two examples, Cavallino's style as a draughtsman was just as soft and pictorial as one would expect from his pictures.

PROVENANCE: Giovanni Piancastelli (no mark, see Lugt S. 2078a); Mr. and Mrs. Edward Brandegee (no mark, see Lugt 1860c).

BIBLIOGRAPHY: Janos Scholz, "Sei- and Settecento Drawings in Venice: Notes on Two Exhibitions and a Publication," *Art Quarterly,* XXIII, 1960, p. 62, fig. 10; Walter Vitzthum, "Neapolitan Seicento Drawings in Florida," *Burlington Magazine,* CIII, 1961, p. 314; Oreste Ferrari, "Seicento Napoletano a Sarasota," *Napoli Nobilissima,* I, 1961–1962, p. 237; Walter Vitzthum, "Drawings from the Scholz Collection in Germany," *Master Drawings,* I, no. 4, 1963, p. 59.

EXHIBITIONS: Sarasota, The Ringling Museums, "Baroque Painters of Naples," 1961, no. 62, repr.; Scholz Exhibitions: Columbia, S.C., 1961, no. 24; Hamburg, 1963, no. 38, pl. 68; New Haven, 1964, no. 58.

Janos Scholz

Domenico Maria Canuti

Bologna 1620–Bologna 1684

110 *Jupiter Astride His Eagle, with Psyche and a Putto*

Pen and brown ink, brown wash, heightened with white, over black chalk. 9½ × 13½ inches (24 × 34.3 cm.). The sheet has been pieced out at left and upper margins so that it measures 10 11/16 × 14 5/16 inches (27.1 × 36.3 cm.). Lined.

Inscribed in brown ink in an old hand at lower left, partially cut away: *Domenico Maria Canuti scolare del guid*[o]. A twenty-four-line inscription can be seen showing through from the verso, but cannot be read, as the drawing has been lined.

This representation of a majestic Jupiter astride his eagle, executed with electric dynamism of pen and fluid wash, is a preparatory drawing for the figure of the god in the ceiling fresco of a large room on the *piano nobile* of the Palazzo Altieri in Rome, immediately adjacent to the Great Hall where Carlo Maratti was already at work (see Nos. 111–114). Canuti is said to have begun his fresco late in 1675, and payments are recorded in 1676 (Armando Schiavo, *The Altieri Palace,* Rome, n.d., p. 102). Between the drawing and the fresco, the artist made several changes, notably the alteration of the position of the god's left arm and the reversal of the direction of the feminine figure, probably Psyche, at his right. The outlines of Jupiter's wind-filled draperies and another figure on the right are only roughly suggested in rapid pen strokes.

The sheet has been pieced out at the left and upper margins, and the drawing competently extended at the points of Jupiter's right wrist and the woman's head, in part or possibly wholly by Canuti himself. The extension of Jupiter's hand on the Morgan sheet includes a thunderbolt that in the fresco is held by a putto on Jupiter's left. Ebria Feinblatt (*Art Quarterly,* XV, 1952, p. 53) speculates that the prominence of the thunderbolt in the fresco "may signify that the subject represents some theme of clemency, since the symbol, in seventeenth century iconography, was a sign of this indulgence; and this would accord with the celebration of the name of the Altieri pope, Clement X, as effected, too, in Maratti's *Triumph of Clemency* in the Great Hall, dated 1673–76." Miss Feinblatt has recently discovered that the Uffizi drawing Inv. 20261 F, which formerly she had proposed as a preliminary idea for the Altieri Jupiter group, is the work of Canuti's pupil Giovanni Battista Caccioli (1623–1675). Her new findings will shortly be published in *Master Drawings*.

PROVENANCE: Alliance des Arts (Lugt 61); purchased by the Morgan Library in London, 1962.

BIBLIOGRAPHY: Morgan Library, *Thirteenth Fellows Report, 1963–1964*, p. 100.

EXHIBITIONS: London, P. & D. Colnaghi, "Old Master Drawings," 1962, no. 5; Detroit, Italy 1600–1700, 1965, no. 115.

The Pierpont Morgan Library
1962.12

Carlo Maratti

Camerano 1625–Rome 1713

111 *Allegorical Figure of Divine Wisdom*

Red chalk. 17⅝ × 14½ inches (44.8 × 36.8 cm.). Lined.

Numbered in pen and brown ink at upper left corner, n^o *28*; inscribed on a piece of the old mount pasted to verso, *Carlo Maratti*.

During the pontificate of Clement X Altieri (1670–1676) the pope's family palace on the Piazza del Gesù in Rome was enlarged and extensively redecorated. A major addition to the palace was the Great Hall on the *piano nobile*, and Carlo Maratti, by then the most official and successful of Roman painters, received the commission to decorate this room. Payments are recorded from 1674 to 1677 (Armando Schiavo, *The Altieri Palace*, Rome, n.d., pp. 98–99), but only the fresco that fills the rather long and narrow central section of the vault was executed. This central area is filled with an elaborate allegorical composition dominated by the figure of Clemency, an allusion to the name and virtue of Clement X (repr. Rudolf Wittkower, *Art and Architecture in Italy 1600 to 1750*, 2nd rev. ed., Baltimore, 1965, pl. 128). The rest of the vault, i.e. the steeply curved sections pierced by windows that run from the stucco frame of the allegory of Clemency down to the cornice, were left blank,

but we know from Bellori that **Maratti** intended to decorate these spaces. Bellori further tells us that he himself supplied Maratti with the subjects of these projected frescoes, and that the artist prepared *elegantissimi disegni d'ogni figura*. The undecorated portions of the vault were divided by windows into eight sections, two at each end of the Great Hall, and three on each long wall. The four sections of the vaulting at the opposite ends of the Hall were to contain, Bellori informs us, allegorical figures representing Religion, Faith, Divine Wisdom, and Evangelical Truth, respectively. Working from Bellori's descriptions of these subjects, Francis Dowley identified three preparatory drawings by Maratti for these never-executed frescoes: an *Allegory of Religion*, an *Allegory of Christian Faith*, both in the Ashmolean Museum, Oxford, and an *Allegory of Evangelical Truth* in the Louvre (F. H. Dowley, *Burlington Magazine*, CI, 1959, pp. 71–73, figs. 30, 36, and 35, respectively). To these three drawings may be added a further study for the *Allegory of Evangelical Truth* in the Ashmolean Museum (Parker, *Ashmolean Catalogue*, II, no. 923, mistakenly attributed to Giuseppe Passeri). The present fine drawing, which only very recently reappeared, is identifiable as a preparatory study by Maratti for the *Allegory of Divine Wisdom*. Bellori's description of this subject runs roughly thus: Divine Wisdom holds a scepter, as governess of the Universe, and the book with the seven signs of the Apocalypse containing the Mysteries, and near her an angry putto drives away Faithless Ignorance (Bellori, Piacentini edition, p. 93). In the drawing the enthroned crowned female figure holding book and scepter, her head surrounded by a blaze of light, is clearly Divine Wisdom. Here Maratti has been inspired by his master Andrea Sacchi's representation of the same figure seated in a curved throne, painted in the Palazzo Barberini more than thirty years earlier (see No. 73 of the exhibition). The curved, half-lunette shape of the design, as well as the molding and console indicated at the right, make it clear that the drawing was intended for one of the oddly shaped vaulted areas at the ends of the room, in this case immediately to the left of a semicircular window. The angry putto of

Bellori's description may be recognized at the left, and Faithless Ignorance, a sensuously Cortonesque kneeling female figure, is identified by long ass's ears that are only lightly indicated here.

PROVENANCE: Thomas Hudson (Lugt 2432); Sir Joshua Reynolds (Lugt 2364); Prince Wladimir Nikolaevitch Argoutinsky-Dolgoroukoff (according to inscription on verso of old mount); purchased by the Metropolitan Museum in Paris, 1966.

The Metropolitan Museum of Art
Rogers Fund, 66.137

112 *Virtue Crowned by Honor*

Pen and brown ink, heightened with white, over red chalk, on blue paper. 5⅞ × 5⁵⁄₁₆ inches (15 × 13.4 cm.). Upper margin repaired. Lined.

Numbered in pen and brown ink at lower left, *9* (?).

The six spandrels along the long walls of the Great Hall of the Palazzo Altieri were, according to Bellori (see No. 111), to have been painted by Maratti with representations of Rome and the Tiber, Peace, and Virtue Crowned by Honor on one side, and representations of the Four Parts of the World were to be fitted into the three spandrels on the other side. Walter Vitzthum identified preparatory studies for two of the spandrels. He convincingly related the present drawing, No. 114 below, two studies in the Albertina, and a double-faced sheet in the National Gallery of Scotland, to the projected representation of Virtue Crowned by Honor. The compositional solutions investigated in this group of drawings vary considerably, though the subject is always the same: Heroic Christian Virtue, who has adopted Hercules' attributes of club and lion skin, is crowned by Honor, represented as a winged youth who holds a palm branch and in some cases, as here, a cornucopia as well as a crown. Vitzthum recognized that a drawing at Darmstadt was a study for the spandrel with Rome and the Tiber. Another Maratti drawing for this spandrel is at Bowdoin College (repr. *Burlington Magazine*, CV, 1963, p. 511). Keith Andrews has very recently identified a red chalk drawing in the collection of the Earl of Crawford and Balcarres as a study for

the spandrel with an allegorical figure of Africa, one of the Four Parts of the World.

PROVENANCE: Richard Houlditch (Lugt 2214); purchased by the Metropolitan Museum in London, 1961.

BIBLIOGRAPHY: Walter Vitzthum, "Drawings by Carlo Maratta for the Altieri Palace in Rome," *Burlington Magazine*, CV, 1963, pp. 367–370, fig. 32.

The Metropolitan Museum of Art
Rogers Fund, 61.169

113 *Virtue Crowned by Honor*

Red chalk. 13½ × 10⁹⁄₁₆ inches (34.3 × 26.8 cm.). Repair at left margin; spots at lower margin. Lined.

Inscribed in pen and brown ink at lower left corner, *Carlo Maratt*.

A more elaborate study, with a number of variations from the previous design, for the spandrel of this subject in the Great Hall of the Palazzo Altieri. In one of the preparatory drawings in the Albertina for this spandrel Virtue points to Cerberus who is chained at her feet, in front of a supporting console. This console is not included in the previous preparatory drawing (No. 112), but Vitzthum contends that Virtue's gesture, pointing down with her right hand, presupposes there the presence of Cerberus below. We know from Bellori's description that in Maratti's final projects Cerberus appeared not below Virtue and Honor, but was chained at the feet of Peace. Thus at some stage of the planning Maratti shifted the animal from one spandrel to another. The present study must be close to the definitive solution for the Virtue and Honor spandrel. Instead of pointing down at Cerberus, Virtue raises her right arm more in accordance with Bellori's text, where Virtue and Honor "reach out toward each other with their hands." Cerberus, however, is still about in this project; his three heads are lightly indicated against the top of the console, at the lower margin. On the verso of the Edinburgh sheet of studies we find the two figures posed very much as in the present drawing, but Cerberus is there omitted.

PROVENANCE: Miss Clinton; sale, London, Sotheby's, December 1, 1964, no. 37, repr., bought by the Metropolitan Museum.

BIBLIOGRAPHY: Walter Vitzthum, "Drawings by Carlo

Maratta for the Palazzo Altieri in Rome," *Burlington Magazine*, CV, 1963, p. 368, note 11.

The Metropolitan Museum of Art
Purchase, Joseph Pulitzer Bequest, 64.295.1

114 *Peace*

Pen and brown ink, brown and a little gray wash, heightened with white, over red chalk, on brownish paper. 9½ × 9³⁄₁₆ inches (24.1 × 23.3 cm.). Lined.

Numbered in pen and brown ink at lower left, *N. 15.*

Another newly identified project by Maratti for the unexecuted parts of the decoration of the Great Hall in the Palazzo Altieri. With the exception of an important detail, this drawing corresponds with Bellori's description of one of the projected spandrels along the long walls of the Hall: "Peace brought to the world through the Incarnation of Christ, with the fettered fury of Avernus at her feet; she holds in one hand an olive branch, and points with the other towards an angel who explains the legend *Et in terra Pax.*" (Bellori, Piacentini edition, p. 93). In the drawing not Cerberus, the fettered fury of Avernus, but a manacled prisoner cringing on what appears to be a pile of military equipment, is seen at the feet of Peace. This discrepancy need not disturb us, for it has been noted in the previous entry that Cerberus at some stage simply changed place along the wall, moving from the feet of Virtue to the feet of Peace. The drawing thus records an early and not the definitive scheme for the Peace spandrel. At the top of the triangular design parallel lines and a circle suggest a coffered ceiling seen in steep perspective from below. Such indications appear in many of Maratti's projects for the decoration of sections of the vaulting of the Great Hall, and they also occur in a pen drawing in the Metropolitan Museum (65.206), recently identified by Vitzthum as a sketch for the whole ceiling scheme, including the nude figures that Maratti painted in monochrome at the corners of the central composition. Maratti must thus have intended the Allegory of Clemency to appear as a framed *quadro riportato*, surrounded by allegorical groups and seen in a setting of illusionistic architecture. The present drawing was once attributed to Marat-

ti's pupil, Giuseppe Passeri; the confusion is understandable, for the pupil's handling of pen and red chalk derives directly from his master's manner (see No. 138).

PROVENANCE: Sir Karl T. Parker; purchased by the Metropolitan Museum in London, 1966.

The Metropolitan Museum of Art
Rogers Fund, 66.53.3

115 *Jael Slaying Sisera*

Red chalk, heightened with white, on blue paper. 8¹³⁄₁₆ × 10¹³⁄₁₆ inches (22.4 × 27.4 cm.). Crease at lower right corner. Lined.

About 1677, Maratti was commissioned to supply cartoons for the mosaic decoration of the vault of the second bay of the left nave of St. Peter's in Rome, immediately adjacent to the Chapel of the Presentation. Work on the cartoons and on the mosaics progressed slowly; the four pendentives with representations of Aaron, Noah, Gideon, and Isaiah, and the six half-lunettes representing Judith and Holofernes, Jael and Sisera, Joshua, Elijah, Moses, and Miriam were completed between 1686 and 1695. The cupola with its representation of St. John's vision of the Immaculate Conception was still unfinished at Maratti's death in 1713 (Mezzetti, p. 344). The artist's cartoons for the six half-lunettes are preserved in the Loggia della Benedizione of St. Peter's. The cartoon for the Jael and Sisera composition (repr. Mezzetti, p. 268) reveals Maratti's final solution for the pose of the biblical heroine Jael: as in the present preparatory study, she holds the hammer in her right hand, but instead of holding up the tent spike in her left hand she points down at the body of the Canaanite general Sisera, whose head she has already pierced with the spike. A large number of preparatory studies for the Jael and Sisera group, offering alternative compositional solutions, have survived. Mezzetti and Schaar have discussed those at Düsseldorf, Berlin, and Melbourne, while Blunt and Cooke have catalogued the studies at Windsor. More recently a sizable group of sketches in Madrid has been published by V. M. Nieto Alcaide (*Dibujos de la Real Academia de San Fernando. Carlo Maratti.*

Cuarenta y tres dibujos de tema religioso, Madrid, 1965). The present drawing is an excellent example of Maratti's late chalk style, where heavy plastic form is indicated with great assurance in a broad and abbreviated manner. The Metropolitan Museum also possesses one of the many surviving studies for the pendant half-lunette, where Judith is represented holding the head of Holofernes (62.133; repr. *Master Drawings*, III, no. 2, 1965, pl. 37b).

PROVENANCE: John, Lord Northwick; Northwick sale, London, Sotheby's, November 1–4, 1920, no. 64; Henry Oppenheimer, London; Oppenheimer sale, London, Christie's, July 10–14, 1936, no. 120, bought by the Metropolitan Museum.

BIBLIOGRAPHY: Harry B. Wehle, "Four Drawings," *Metropolitan Museum of Art Bulletin*, January 1937, pp. 6–9; Metropolitan Museum, *European Drawings*, I, repr. no. 32; Amalia Mezzetti, "Contributi a Carlo Maratti," *Rivista dell'Istituto Nazionale d'Archeologia e Storia dell'Arte*, n.s., IV, 1955, p. 339; Blunt and Cooke, *Roman Drawings at Windsor*, p. 57 (wrongly said to be in the Morgan Library).

EXHIBITIONS: Detroit, Italy 1600–1700, 1965, no. 57, repr.

The Metropolitan Museum of Art
Harris Brisbane Dick Fund, 36.101.2

116 *The Virgin Immaculate and Four Male Saints*

Pen and brown ink, brown wash, over black chalk; accidental smudges of red chalk. 15 11/16 × 7⅞ inches (39.8 × 20 cm.). Top of sheet cut to the shape of an arch. Small oil stain at upper left. Watermark: fleur-de-lis in a circle.

Inscribed in pen and brown ink at lower right, *Cav. Carlo Maratti.*

Verso: Black chalk sketch of St. John the Evangelist, St. Augustine, and St. John Chrysostom.

For the Cybo chapel of S. Maria del Popolo in Rome, Carlo Maratti painted an altarpiece representing St. John the Evangelist, St. Gregory, St. John Chrysostom, and St. Augustine anachronistically grouped together and engaged in a discussion of the doctrine of the Immaculate Conception, which is symbolically represented above them. The picture, a stately example of Maratti's mature style, was commissioned by Cardinal Alderano Cybo and was finished in 1686. An unusually complete series of preparatory drawings for the altarpiece has survived, and through the alternative composi-

tional solutions that Maratti investigated, we can observe the caution and the high seriousness of the artist's working methods. The present drawing and a design in Düsseldorf come closest to the finished picture; composition sketches in the Metropolitan Museum (see No. 117 below), Chatsworth, the Uffizi, at Windsor Castle, and in Madrid (the latter recently published by V. M. Nieto Alcaide, *Dibujos de la Real Academia de San Fernando. Carlo Maratti. Cuarenta y tres dibujos de tema religioso*, Madrid, 1965), record important variations. Studies for individual figures in the altarpiece are in the British Museum, the Berlin Print Room, the Kunstmuseum at Düsseldorf, and in the collection of John Pope-Hennessy in London.

PROVENANCE: Jonathan Richardson Senior (Lugt 2184); Sir Charles Greville (Lugt 549); Earls of Warwick (Lugt 2600); Charles Fairfax Murray; purchased by J. Pierpont Morgan in London, 1910.

BIBLIOGRAPHY: Fairfax Murray, IV, no. 183, repr.; Francis H. Dowley, "Some Maratti Drawings at Düsseldorf," *Art Quarterly*, XX, 1957, pp. 171–174, fig. 13; Blunt and Cooke, *Roman Drawings at Windsor*, p. 56; Bean, *100 European Drawings*, under no. 37; Brigitte Heinzl, "The Luti Collection," *Connoisseur*, CLXI, 1966, p. 20 (where it is suggested that the drawing once belonged to Benedetto Luti; the presence of the mark of Richardson Senior on the sheet makes this unlikely).

The Pierpont Morgan Library
No. IV, 183

117 *The Virgin Immaculate and Four Male Saints*

Pen and brown ink, red chalk, and a little red wash. 17 13/16 × 10¼ inches (45.3 × 26 cm.). Arched top torn irregularly; slight repairs in brush and gray wash in another hand at top of arch. Lined.

Inscribed in pen and brown ink at lower left, *C° Maratti.*

Study for the altarpiece in the Cybo chapel of S. Maria del Popolo, Rome (see No. 116 above). The Metropolitan Museum possesses another sketch, executed in red chalk, for this picture (62.137).

PROVENANCE: William Mayor (Lugt 2799); C. R. Rudolf (Lugt S. 2811b); purchased by the Metropolitan Museum in London, 1963.

BIBLIOGRAPHY: K. T. Parker, "Carlo Maratti," *Old Master Drawings*, X, no. 39, 1935, p. 46, pl. 45; Amalia Mezzetti, "Contributi a Carlo Maratti," *Rivista dell'Istituto*

Nazionale d'Archeologia e Storia dell'Arte, n.s., IV, 1955, p. 337; Francis H. Dowley, "Some Maratti Drawings at Düsseldorf," *Art Quarterly*, XX, 1957, pp. 171–174; Bean, *100 European Drawings*, no. 37, repr.

EXHIBITIONS: Leicester Museum and Art Gallery, "Old Master Drawings," 1952, no. 40; London, Arts Council, "Old Master Drawings from the Collection of Mr. C. R. Rudolf," 1962, no. 36.

The Metropolitan Museum of Art
Rogers Fund, 63.18

Francesco Castiglione

Died Genoa 1716

118 *A Congress of Animals*

Pen and brown ink, watercolor, over traces of black chalk. 8¼ × 12³⁄₁₆ inches (21 × 31 cm.).

Inscribed in pen and black ink at lower margin, *Francesco Castiglione Genovese.*

Francesco, son of Giovanni Benedetto Castiglione, re-emerges as a distinct artistic personality thanks to the attribution neatly marked on the sheet. The inscription is in the "Reliable Venetian Hand," that of an anonymous collector of the mid-eighteenth century who was remarkably accurate in his identifications. As a painter Francesco repeated his father's compositions, in lighter, brighter colors; as a draughtsman he here substitutes a light pen line and transparent watercolor for the rich oil paint so lavishly and effectively brushed on paper by his father. The subject, a motley group of animals that form a peaceable kingdom, is typically Genoese and reflects the persistent influence of Flemish animal painting in Liguria. The Metropolitan Museum possesses another watercolor drawing, representing a seated youth and dogs in a landscape, also convincingly attributed to Francesco in the "Reliable Venetian Hand" (08.227.24, repr. Bettagno, fig. 49).

Janos Scholz owns a sheet by the same artist, representing a hunter with his dogs; this drawing bears an attribution of uncertain date to Francesco Casanova (1727–1802), whose drawing style is quite different, French and Dutch in inspiration and fully eighteenth century. A drawing of animals entering the ark, attributed to G. B. Castiglione when in Vivant Denon's collection, appears from a litho-

graphic reproduction to be the work of his son Francesco (*Monuments*, III, pl. 231).

PROVENANCE: "Reliable Venetian Hand" (Lugt S. 3005c–d); Benjamin West (Lugt 419); William Esdaile (Lugt 2617); purchased by the Metropolitan Museum in London, 1908.

BIBLIOGRAPHY: Alessandro Bettagno, *Disegni di una collezione veneziano del settecento* (exhibition catalogue), Venice, Cini Foundation, 1966, p. 54, pl. 50 (though the drawing did not figure in the exhibition).

The Metropolitan Museum of Art
Rogers Fund, 08.227.25

Domenico Piola

Genoa 1628–Genoa 1703

119 *The Rest on the Flight into Egypt*

Brush, brown and gray wash, heightened with white, over black chalk, on gray-green paper. 10⁵⁄₁₆ × 15¼ inches (26.3 × 38.7 cm.).

Domenico Piola was a prolific draughtsman, and, in addition to preparatory studies for pictures and frescoes, he produced great numbers of drawings that were ends in themselves, no doubt intended for sale to collectors. In this he followed the example of Giovanni Benedetto Castiglione, whose influence is also apparent in the pastoral mood of this highly finished *Rest on the Flight*. This fine example is the kind of Piola drawing that was much admired and imitated in eighteenth-century France. Eloisa Malagoli suggests a connection between the drawing and a picture by Domenico Piola representing the Rest on the Flight, in the Palazzo Bianco, Genoa, though the latter is a nocturnal scene.

BIBLIOGRAPHY: Eloisa Malagoli, "The Drawings of Casa Piola," *Burlington Magazine*, CVIII, 1966, p. 508, fig. 33.

EXHIBITIONS: Dayton, Genoese Masters, 1962–1963, no. 93, repr.; New York, Finch College, Genoese Painters, no. 70, repr.

Robert and Bertina Suida Manning

120 *Time and a Woman Holding the Sun and the Moon*

Brush and brown wash, over black chalk. 11¹³⁄₁₆ × 16⅞ inches (30 × 42.8 cm.).

Inscribed in black chalk at lower left, *P.*

Piola proposes alternative solutions for grouping the two figures in a roundel. The drawing, a particularly luminous example of Piola's facile draughtsmanship, is probably a study for one of the frescoed decorations he undertook in Genoa.

PROVENANCE: Mr. and Mrs. Edward Brandegee (Lugt S. 1860c).

BIBLIOGRAPHY: "Italian Drawings from the Collection of Janos Scholz," *Metropolitan Museum of Art Bulletin*, May 1965, Part II, p. 341, repr.

EXHIBITIONS: Columbia, S.C., Scholz Exhibition, 1961, no. 65, repr.; Dayton, Genoese Masters, 1962–1963, no. 91, repr.; Hamburg, Scholz Exhibition, 1963, no. 115, pl. 64; Detroit, Italy 1600–1700, 1965, no. 180, repr.; New York, Finch College, Genoese Painters, 1964–1965, no. 68, repr.

Janos Scholz

Bartolomeo Biscaino

Genoa 1632–Genoa 1657

121 *The Rest on the Flight into Egypt*

Red chalk, white gouache, and touches of graphite. 11⅞ × 8⅜ inches (30.2 × 21.4 cm.). Small loss and circular stain at lower center. Lined.

Inscribed on verso of lining in pencil, *Bartolomeo Biscaino*; in pen and brown ink, *Mariette*.

This is a typical example of the facile graceful style of the Genoese painter and etcher who died of the plague before he was twenty-five years old. Biscaino almost invariably uses red chalk generously heightened with whites applied with the brush as he does here. His etchings are with few exceptions devoted to religious subjects; the present composition does not appear among them.

While the inscription of Mariette's name on the verso of the sheet may be an indication of his past ownership of the drawing, it is not among those listed in the sale catalogue of 1775.

PROVENANCE: Thomas Dimsdale (Lugt 2426); Charles Fairfax Murray; purchased by J. Pierpont Morgan in London, 1910.

BIBLIOGRAPHY: Fairfax Murray, IV, no. 195, repr.

*The Pierpont Morgan Library
No. IV, 195*

Crescenzio Onofri

Rome 1632–Florence 1698(?)

122 *Landscape*

Pen and brown ink, over traces of black chalk. 8 × 11¼ inches (20.4 × 28.5 cm.). Watermark: heraldic mountain composed of three hills, surmounted by a cross.

Inscribed in pen and brown ink on strip of paper pasted along lower margin of sheet, *Di Crescenzio Onofrij*; on verso, *Al Sig^r Ferdinando Maria Melli, Crescentio Onofrij Dona l'Anno 1705 Genaio*.

Pascoli reports that Crescenzio Onofri was Gaspard Dughet's only pupil, and the little we know of Onofri's work confirms this dependence on Dughet. Recently Ilara Toesca has published landscape frescoes by Onofri in the Castello Theodoli at S. Vito Romano (*Paragone*, XI, no. 125, 1960, figs. 30–32b), frescoes that are documented as Onofri's works by his own engravings of them. The neat, elegant style of the present drawing, bearing an old attribution to Onofri, indeed suggests an engraver's hand. Other landscape drawings similar in style to this sheet and traditionally attributed to the artist are at Windsor (Blunt and Cooke, *Roman Drawings at Windsor*, nos. 553, 554) and at Holkham Hall. The old inscription on the verso of the drawing is puzzling: most sources record 1698 as Onofri's death date, but here is a sheet presented, if the notation is correct, by the artist to a certain Ferdinando Maria Melli in 1705.

PROVENANCE: Purchased by the Metropolitan Museum in New York, 1963.

*The Metropolitan Museum of Art
Rogers Fund, 63.222*

Luca Giordano

Naples 1632–Naples 1705

123 *Neptune Triumphant*

Red chalk and red wash. 7¾ × 15⅜ inches (19.6 × 39.1 cm.).

Inscribed on verso in pencil, *L. Giordano 20*.

Luca Giordano's earliest drawings are done in an abbreviated, scratchy, and angular style that owes much to Ribera. Intelligent abbreviation remained a characteristic of his draughtsmanship throughout his long career, but scratchy angularity was soon replaced by a suave use of transparent washes over lightly indicated chalk contour lines, as here, where the drawing has a brio and lightness that look forward to the eighteenth century. It has been suggested that this drawing is a study for part of Giordano's ceiling fresco in the Palazzo Medici-Riccardi, Florence, but there a group of figures dominated by Neptune riding in triumph is quite differently composed; furthermore, the indication of a cartouche-like frame at the right in the drawing would seem to exclude a connection with the Riccardi ceiling, where the space is treated as a single area, uninterrupted by architectural divisions.

PROVENANCE: Unidentified collector's mark at lower right.

BIBLIOGRAPHY: Walter Vitzthum, "Neapolitan Seicento Drawings in Florida," *Burlington Magazine*, CIII, 1961, pp. 314–317, fig. 23; Oreste Ferrari, "Seicento Napoletano a Sarasota," *Napoli Nobilissima*, I, 1961–1962, p. 237, fig. 28.

EXHIBITIONS: Sarasota, The Ringling Museums, "Baroque Painters of Naples," 1961, no. 70, repr. p. 61; Scholz Exhibitions: Columbia, S.C., 1961, no. 42; Hamburg, 1963, no. 70, pl. 63; New Haven, 1964, no. 62.

Janos Scholz

124 *The Last Judgment*

Black chalk, brush, and gray wash. 19 15/16 × 14 3/8 inches (50.6 × 36.6 cm.). Spot of brown oil paint to left of center. Lower corners replaced; horizontal creases at center; various repaired tears.

Inscribed in pen and brown ink at lower center, *Lucas Jordanus f.^e*

Verso: Black chalk study of flying skeletons.

For ten years, from 1692 to 1702, Giordano was court painter to Charles II of Spain. His first and principal commission was the decoration of the vaults of the vast church of the Escorial near Madrid, a task begun more than a century before but left incomplete by the Genoese decorator Luca Cambiaso. Walter Vitzthum and Oreste Ferrari have independently identified this sheet, a typical example of Giordano's draughtsmanship during his Spanish period, as a study for part of *The Last*

Judgment painted on the vault of the west arm of the church that connects the central crossing with the two-storied choir situated at the opposite end of the church from the high altar. The unfailing brilliance of Giordano's decorative style is apparent in this drawing; movement, light, and color are suggested by summary chalk outlines brought to life by painterly touches of transparent gray wash. An old copy of the drawing is in the Albertina (repr. *Beschreibender Katalog der Handzeichnungen in der Staatlichen Graphischen Sammlung Albertina*, VI, 1941, no. 697, as Neapolitan, mid-eighteenth century).

BIBLIOGRAPHY: Walter Vitzthum, "Le Dessin baroque à Naples," *L'Oeil*, no. 97, 1963, p. 88, repr. p. 51 (where the drawing was mistakenly associated with Giordano's frescoes in the sacristy of the cathedral at Toledo); Oreste Ferrari, "Drawings by Luca Giordano in the British Museum," *Burlington Magazine*, CVIII, 1966, p. 301.

EXHIBITIONS: Durham, North Carolina, Duke University, "Italian Master Drawings from the Collection of Mrs. Richard Krautheimer," 1966, no. 23.

Mrs. Richard Krautheimer

125 *The Triumph of Cybele*

Brush and brown wash over black chalk. 14 3/4 × 21 inches (37.5 × 53.3 cm.). Vertical crease just left of center; missing passage replaced at center of lower margin.

Inscribed in brush and gray wash at right margin, *Jorda . . .*; in pen and brown ink at lower margin, *N.º 72, 324 ps, 4 . . . 28*.

Walter Vitzthum has recently pointed out that this figure of the earth goddess Cybele, crowned with city towers, holding a key in her hand, and riding triumphantly in a chariot drawn by lionesses, is a preparatory study for a section of the ceiling fresco in the principal room of the Casón del Buen Retiro in Madrid. The relevant detail of the fresco, which represents the story of the Order of the Golden Fleece, is reproduced by Yves Bottineau in *Gazette des Beaux-Arts*, LVI, 1960, p. 253. The Uffizi possesses a somewhat smaller study for the group of Minerva in full battle regalia and her warlike attendants, seen opposite Cybele in the Buen Retiro ceiling (Uffizi no. 6698 F), and in the Biblioteca

Nacional, Madrid, there is a sketch for another group of mythological figures in the ceiling (no. 7946).

PROVENANCE: Sale, London, Sotheby's, February 27, 1963, no. 21 (as anonymous Italian, seventeenth century), bought by the Metropolitan Museum.

BIBLIOGRAPHY: Bean, *100 European Drawings*, no. 38, repr.

The Metropolitan Museum of Art
Rogers Fund, 63.76.4

Ciro Ferri

Rome 1634–Rome 1689

126 *The Circumcision*

Pen and brown ink, brown wash, heightened with white, over black chalk, on light brown paper. With architectural border, 14⅜ × 9⁷⁄₁₆ inches (36.6 × 24 cm.); without architectural border, 11ⁱ⁄₁₆ × 7⅝ inches (28.1 × 19.4 cm.). Repairs at margins. Lined.

Ciro Ferri, the most gifted of Pietro da Cortona's assistants and imitators, is seen at his best as a draughtsman in highly finished designs for engravings. Pascoli (*Vite de pittori, scultori, ed architetti*, I, Rome, 1730, p. 173) says of these drawings: "meravigliosi son quegli intagliati dallo Spierre, particolarmente la circoncisione del Signore pel messale d'Alessandro VII." This is Ferri's design for the *Circumcision* praised by Pascoli; engraved by François Spierre, it figures as an illustration in a papal missal published in Rome in 1662, during the reign of Alexander VII. The frontispiece of the missal records a design by Pietro da Cortona. Ferri's drawing was reproduced in reverse by Spierre with slight variations; in the engraving the tiara worn by the officiant is omitted, as are the pediment and shell at the top of the frame. The Louvre possesses a red chalk design by Ferri (Inv. 477) in the same direction as the engraving; in this drawing, which bears the *Incidatur* of the ecclesiastical censor, the tiara has been suppressed. In the Metropolitan Museum (61.166.2) there is a fairly exact replica, no doubt an old copy of the present drawing, without the architectural surround.

Donald P. Gurney

Giuseppe Maria Mitelli

Bologna 1634–Bologna 1718

127 *"In His Own House, Each Is King"*

Red chalk, partially pricked for transfer. 9⅜ × 7⅝ inches (23.8 × 19.4 cm.). Lined.

Active principally as a graphic artist, Mitelli was an exponent of the informal aspect of Bolognese art that concerned itself with popular genre, satire, and caricature. Among his best-known works is the series of forty-eight engravings entitled *Proverbj Figurati* (Bologna, 1678. Bartsch, XIX, pp. 293–301, nos. 67–116) for which the Morgan Library recently acquired fourteen preparatory drawings. The study shown is his design for pl. 18, which illustrates the proverb "In casa sua ciascuno è re." The engraving, which is in the reverse of the drawing, also carries the text: "Frà domestici Lari, humile, e parca / La signoria può tutto ciò, che pote, / Sù l'aureo trono, il Regnator Monarca." Mitelli is at his best as a draughtsman in a drawing like this, where he demonstrates what he had learned from his master Guercino. Other drawings in the Morgan series show him working more in the manner of Cantarini, with whom he also studied. The thirteen other drawings are preparatory for pls. 3, 5, 9, 10, 14, 21, 23, 27, 34, 40, 45, 47, and 48.

Mitelli also worked as an engraver after other artists, among them Albani, Carracci, and Guercino.

PROVENANCE: Purchased by the Morgan Library in New York, 1966.

The Pierpont Morgan Library
Gift of the Fellows, 1966.4

Giovanni Battista Beinaschi

Fassano (Turin) 1636–Naples 1688

128 *Two Studies of a Youth Blowing a Trumpet*

Black chalk on blue paper. 15 × 21⅜ inches (38 × 53.7 cm.). Vertical crease at center; several brown stains.

Inscribed in pencil at lower right, *Beinaschi (11) 10*; in pen and brown ink, *D 2* (?).

Verso: Black chalk study of a man looking upward.

Beinaschi, Piedmontese by birth but active in Rome and above all in Naples as a fresco painter, had a broad, vigorous if somewhat coarse drawing style that owes much to Lanfranco. From the eighteenth century onward his drawings, particularly chalk figure studies like the present good and typical example, have been mistakenly attributed to Lanfranco himself. Comparison between Mr. Scholz's beautiful head study by Lanfranco (No. 32) and this Beinaschi drawing from his collection shows the points of contact and the differences between the two artists as draughtsmen. Lanfranco models his form with short nervous parallel strokes; contours, when indicated, tend to be angular, and plasticity is suggested in an abbreviated manner by white highlights. In the drawings of Beinaschi Lanfranco's forms have been blown up to a larger scale, and the chalk line has grown soft and rather superficial. Beinaschi was an exceptionally prolific draughtsman; in New York further examples of his work are to be found in the Scholz collection, the Cooper Union Museum (1958–143–25, attributed to Giacinto Brandi), and the Metropolitan Museum (66.49).

PROVENANCE: Giovanni Piancastelli (no mark, see Lugt S. 2078a); Mr. and Mrs. Edward Brandegee (no mark, see Lugt S. 1860c).

BIBLIOGRAPHY: Jacob Bean and Walter Vitzthum, "Disegni del Lanfranco e del Benaschi," *Bollettino d'Arte,* XLVI, 1961, p. 121, note 41.

EXHIBITIONS: Hamburg, Scholz Exhibition, 1963, no. 13; Detroit, Italy 1600–1700, 1965, no. 31, repr. p. 49.

Janos Scholz

Andrea Celesti

Venice 1637–Venice 1706

129 *Allegory of Venetian Power*

Pen and brown ink, brown wash, over red chalk. Design proper, 14$\frac{9}{16}$ × 11$\frac{3}{16}$ inches (37 × 28.5 cm.); entire sheet, including an engraved border, 21½ × 15$\frac{15}{16}$ inches (54.5 × 40.5 cm.). Horizontal creases at center and top half; losses at upper right margin. Lined.

Inscribed in pen and brown ink at lower left corner of drawn sheet, *Celesti inventor.*

Eighteenth-century guide books to the city of Brescia describe a now vanished picture that hung in one of the principal rooms of the Palazzo Municipale (La Loggia). In this composition Venice, Queen of the Seas, was represented riding over the waves in a silver conch shell encircled by tribute-bearing figures, with Justice, holding scales, close at hand. This recently rediscovered drawing corresponds in almost every detail with the old descriptions and may well be a preparatory study for the lost picture. The scale of the design and the fact that the artist has used a sheet bearing an engraved architectural border suggest that the drawing may have been made as a *modello* to be shown to the commissioner of the picture. The presence of the old inscription *Celesti inventor* is justified by the style of the sheet, which is comparable to that of the *David and Goliath* in the Morassi collection, recently identified as a study for a picture in the Casa Parisini at Garagnano (see Terisio Pignatti in *La Pittura del seicento a Venezia,* Venice, 1959, catalogue of drawings, no. 83).

PROVENANCE: Purchased by the Metropolitan Museum in London, 1964.

*The Metropolitan Museum of Art
Rogers Fund, 64.13*

Elisabetta Sirani

Bologna 1638–Bologna 1665

130 *The Finding of Moses*

Brush and brown wash, heightened with white, over black chalk, on blue-gray paper; framing lines in black chalk. 19$\frac{5}{8}$ × 13$\frac{1}{16}$ inches (49.9 × 33.1 cm.). Lined.

Like her father Giovanni Andrea, the short-lived Elisabetta Sirani painted in a graceful manner that derives from the mature work of Guido Reni. As a draughtsman she is at her most felicitous when using brush and pale, transparent wash over a black sketch, as in the present example, where the blue-gray of the support is used to great pictorial advantage. Such drawings may be said to be transpositions into another technique of Reni's late, diaphanous, almost monochrome style as a painter. No picture by Elisabetta representing the Finding of Moses is recorded. It is the highly personal style of the drawing that justifies the presumably traditional attribution; other similar wash drawings by the artist are at Windsor (see Kurz, *Bolognese Drawings at Windsor*, pls. 71–73) and in the Louvre.

PROVENANCE: Purchased by the Metropolitan Museum in New York, 1962.

EXHIBITIONS: London, Alpine Club Gallery, "Old Master Drawings and Early English Watercolours Presented by Yvonne ffrench," 1961, no. 30.

*The Metropolitan Museum of Art
Rogers Fund, 62.21*

Giovanni Battista Gaulli, called Baciccio

Genoa 1639–Rome 1709

131 *Joseph's Dream*

Pen and dark brown ink, brown wash, heightened with white, over black chalk indications, on buff paper. 10¾ × 8 inches (27.4 × 20.3 cm.). Lined.

Inscribed on mount in pen and brown ink, *Gio. Battista Gauli, detto Bacciccia*; at lower right, *91 / 74–4*; on verso of mount at upper left corner, *1005*.

This drawing and the painting of another night scene with which it is best compared, the artist's Fermo altarpiece now in the Palazzo Spinola, Genoa, representing the Adoration of the Shepherds (repr. Robert Enggass, *The Painting of Baciccio, Giovanni Battista Gaulli, 1639–1709*, University Park, Pennsylvania, 1964, fig. 32; "c. 1672"), show the impress of Baciccio's trip to Parma (1669), undertaken to study the art of Correggio. The radiance emanating from the Virgin and Child, and the figure of the plunging angel, which the draughtsman discarded in favor of a less precipitous pose, do homage to Correggio's *Madonna della Notte*, now in Dresden, but in Baciccio's day in the ducal collection at Modena, to which he had entry, thanks to letters of introduction from his sponsor Gianlorenzo Bernini. The flickering, broken line is characteristic of the artist at this period; the manner of piling up masses of convoluted drapery folds in effects that derive from Bernini's sculpture is a hallmark of his style. The drawing illustrates Matthew 2:13.

PROVENANCE: Charles Rogers (Lugt 624).

EXHIBITIONS: Dayton, Genoese Masters, 1962–1963, no. 84, repr.; New York, Finch College, Genoese Painters,

1964–1965, no. 76; Detroit, Italy 1600–1700, 1965, no. 52, repr.

Robert and Bertina Suida Manning

132 *Allegory of the Mathematical Sciences*

Pen and brown ink, brown and gray wash, over black chalk. 11⅝ × 10¼ inches (29.5 × 26 cm.). Repaired losses in lower right corner; small losses at lower left margin and upper left; vertical break at upper left. Lined.

Numbered in pen and black ink at upper left, *44*; inscribed on old mount at lower left, *Pietro da Cortona*.

Gaulli's design, as Enggass noted, was engraved by Robert van Audenaerd (1663–1743). The engraving, possibly intended as a book illustration, is in the reverse of the drawing, so that the female figure of the print properly carries the compasses in her right hand and Mercury points the way with his right arm. The subject has been tentatively described as an "Allegory of Learning (?)" and as an "Allegory of the Liberal Arts (?)," broad interpretations of the female figure and her small companion whose attributes seem to identify them only with the mathematical sciences (all of the quadrivium except music, which, of course, might be present in the figure of Mercury). It might be added that Goltzius's engraved figure of Urania, the muse of astronomy (Bartsch, III, p. 46, no. 154), shows a seated female figure holding the compasses and the globe, with two books and a square and a rule at her feet, a gathering of attributes very similar to those in the Manning composition.

Enggass suggested a date for the drawing some time between 1685, the year Gaulli completed his remarkable frescoes for the vaults of the Gesù in Rome, and about 1690. It most likely was not earlier since the young Flemish painter and engraver from Ghent apparently did not arrive in Rome until 1685.

PROVENANCE: Mr. and Mrs. Edward Brandegee (Lugt S. 1860c).

BIBLIOGRAPHY: Robert Enggass, *The Painting of Baciccio, Giovanni Battista Gaulli, 1639–1709*, University Park, Pennsylvania, 1964, pp. 73, 113, note 88.

EXHIBITIONS: Dayton, Genoese Masters, 1962–1963, no. 83, repr.; New York, Finch College, Genoese Painters, 1964–1965, no. 75; Detroit, Italy 1600–1700, 1965, no. 53.

Robert and Bertina Suida Manning

Gregorio de' Ferrari

Porto Maurizio 1647–Genoa 1726

133 The Infant Bacchus and an Infant Satyr with a Lion

Black chalk. 11¼ × 8⅛ inches (28.7 × 20.6 cm.). Lightly foxed. Lined.

Inscribed in pen and black ink at lower right, *Greg⁰ De-ferrari*.

Like the young Gaulli (see No. 131), the twenty-two-year-old Gregorio de' Ferrari went to Parma in 1669, and his four years there similarly infused his style with a Correggesque element that finds an echo here in the head of the small satyr. On his return to Genoa, he became assistant and son-in-law to Domenico Piola, whose style he influenced to the extent that their works have on occasion been confused. A freely spiraling column of putti and satyrs mingling with flowers and foliage on the ceiling in the Sala di Fetonte in the Palazzo Rosso at Genoa demonstrates the use to which a drawing like this one might have been put. Such a playful, decorative design foretells the advent of the rococo.

EXHIBITIONS: Dayton, Genoese Masters, 1962–1963, no. 80, repr.; New York, Finch College, Genoese Painters, 1964–1965, no. 80.

Robert and Bertina Suida Manning

Marc Antonio Franceschini

Bologna 1648–Bologna 1729

134 Chastity

Pen and brown ink, gray wash, heightened with white, over black chalk, on brown-washed paper. 15¾ × 11¾ inches (40 × 29.8 cm.).

Study for the frescoed decoration of one of the pendentives under the cupola of the Duomo at Piacenza. In October 1686 Marc Antonio France-schini received the commission, originally offered to Giovanni Battista Gaulli, to decorate the pendentives, two lateral lunettes, and the central arch leading to the choir of the Duomo, and by August 1689 he and his assistant had finished the task. The four pendentives bore figures of Faith, Humility, Charity, and Chastity, respectively. The frescoes in the lateral lunettes represented the Circumcision and the Adoration of the Magi, and the fresco on the central arch the Dream of St. Joseph. During the late nineteenth-century restoration of the Duomo, intended to re-establish the church's original medieval character, Franceschini's frescoes were removed, transferred to canvas, and eventually stored in the refectory of a local monastery where, with the exception of the *Dream of Joseph*, they were destroyed by an aerial bomb in World War II. Fortunately the transferred frescoes had been photographed before the war, and Dwight Miller recently published these interesting records (*Bollettino d'Arte*, XLI, 1956, pp. 318–325). The present drawing, one of a series of four studies for the pendentives that reappeared in London in 1962, corresponds with the lost fresco representing Chastity, except that in the latter the putto holding a crystal vase has been replaced by a youth, and at the upper right a putto holding a branch appears. The drawing is far closer to Franceschini's final solution than is a drawing in the Davia-Bargellini collection in Bologna, one of a series of four that record an earlier stage of the artist's designs, involving a greater number of subsidiary figures (repr. Miller, p. 323). At Windsor there is a study for the Charity pendentive; Kurz had associated this scheme with one of Franceschini's later frescoed lunettes in the church of Corpus Domini at Bologna, but Dwight Miller rightly connects it with the lost Piacenza pendentive (Kurz, *Bolognese Drawings at Windsor*, no. 219; Miller, p. 322). Two further drawings for the Piacenza pendentives are in the collection of Harry Sperling, New York.

PROVENANCE: Purchased by the Metropolitan Museum in London, 1963.

The Metropolitan Museum of Art
Rogers Fund, 63.89

135 Scene from the Life of S. Caterina dei Vigri

Pen and brown ink, brown wash, lightly squared in metalpoint. 8¼ × 10¹⁵⁄₁₆ inches (21 × 27.8 cm.). Several losses at upper left corner and top.

Numbered in brown ink at upper right, *213*.

This drawing and another at the Cooper Union Museum (no. 1938–88–6431) are studies for grisaille decorations that once formed part of the great fresco ensemble of Corpus Domini, the convent church of the order of S. Caterina dei Vigri at Bologna. Franceschini contracted for the project in 1689 and completed it, with the assistance of Luigi Quaini and the *quadraturista* Enrico Haffner, in 1696. Since the grisailles were lost in the bombing of 1943, these *modelli* and the related cartoons preserved in the Opera del Duomo at Orvieto are of special significance. The Cooper Union also owns three drawings for surviving portions of the Corpus Domini decorations; other studies for the frescoes are at Windsor (Kurz, *Bolognese Drawings at Windsor*, nos. 211, 217, and 219).

S. Caterina dei Vigri (1413–1463), patroness of Bologna, is said to have performed miraculously on the violin as she lay dying, although she had never played before. The miniature instrument with which Franceschini represented the saint accompanying an angelic choir is still preserved in the church, as is her body.

PROVENANCE: Giovanni Piancastelli (no mark, see Lugt S. 2078a); Mr. and Mrs. Edward Brandegee (no mark, see Lugt S. 1860c).

BIBLIOGRAPHY: Dwight C. Miller, "Important Drawings by Marcantonio Franceschini at Cooper Union," *Art Bulletin*, XLIII, 1961, pp. 133–134, fig. 4; Richard P. Wunder, *Extravagant Drawings of the Eighteenth Century*, New York, 1962, no. 37, repr.

EXHIBITIONS: New York, Cooper Union Museum, "Five Centuries of Drawing," circulated by the American Federation of Arts, 1959–1961, no. 24.

The Cooper Union Museum
1938–88–6432

Giovanni Battista Foggini

Florence 1652–Florence 1725

136 *The Sabine Women Pleading for Peace between the Romans and Sabines*

Pen and brown ink, brown wash, over black chalk, on brownish paper. 15 13/16 × 21 15/16 inches (40.2 × 55.6 cm.). Vertical crease at center. Lined.

Inscribed on verso of old mount in pen and brown ink in Jonathan Richardson Junior's hand (Lugt 2997), *Sabina Mulieres, quarum ex Injuriâ Bellum ortum erat, . . .* (passage from Livy identifying this subject); in another hand, *Luca Giordano d⁰ Fa Presto per la volicita nel dipingere. . . .*

The dash and freedom of the *fa presto* draughtsmanship no doubt account for the mistaken attribution of this large sheet to Luca Giordano. The drawing has gone under this name since the mid-eighteenth century, when it belonged to Jonathan Richardson Junior, but Vitzthum has quite recently and very convincingly suggested that it is the work of the Florentine sculptor Foggini. Foggini's style as a draughtsman is well documented by the 170 sketches that fill his *Giornale*, now in the Uffizi (see Klaus Lankheit, *Rivista d'Arte*, XXXIV, 1959, pp. 55–108); his line is soft and tends to ornamental curves, while Giordano's is vigorously angular. In the present design Foggini has borrowed a composition from Pietro da Cortona, whose style ruled supreme in Florence well into the eighteenth century. Agitated figures form two parallel dramatic diagonal accents in a classical landscape, as they do in Cortona's *Rape of the Sabines* (repr. Briganti, *Cortona*, pl. 115). Further drawings by Foggini are in the Metropolitan Museum (an Apollo and Coronis, 61.174, as well as a group of ornament designs) and the Avery Library at Columbia University (Vitzthum, pl. 38 b).

PROVENANCE: Jonathan Richardson Junior (Lugt 2170); William Bates (Lugt 2604); David Rust; purchased by the Metropolitan Museum in New York, 1961.

BIBLIOGRAPHY: Walter Vitzthum, review of exhibition of drawings from R. Holland collection, at Newcastle upon Tyne, *Master Drawings*, III, no. 2, 1965, p. 177, pl. 39.

The Metropolitan Museum of Art
Rogers Fund, 61.52

Anton Domenico Gabbiani

Florence 1652–Florence 1726

137 *Two Hermit Saints in the Wilderness*

Pen and brown ink, brown wash, over black chalk; correction in white gouache at center. 10$\frac{11}{16}$ × 16$\frac{11}{16}$ inches (27.1 × 42.3 cm.). Lined.

Inscribed on old mount in pencil, *Gabbiani*.

The scene no doubt represents St. Paul the Hermit in conversation with St. Anthony Abbot. Gabbiani's rather restrained style as a draughtsman is essentially traditional and Tuscan; the freer, Cortonesque overtones noticeable in his figures are due to the three years he spent working with Ciro Ferri in Rome, as well as to the predominant influence of Cortona in seventeenth-century Florence.

PROVENANCE: John Thane (Lugt 1544); Sir Thomas Lawrence (Lugt 2445).

EXHIBITIONS: Oakland, Scholz Exhibition, 1961, no. 40, repr.

Janos Scholz

Giuseppe Passeri

Rome 1654–Rome 1714

138 *St. Peter in Prison*

Pen and black ink, heightened with white, over red and a little black chalk, on red-washed paper. 11 × 9 inches (27.9 × 22.8 cm.). Lined.

The extent of Giuseppe Passeri's debt as a draughtsman to his master Carlo Maratti is apparent when this drawing is compared with one of Maratti's pen studies for the Altieri ceiling (No. 114 of this exhibition). The agitated pen work, the reiterated contours, the pictorial use of white highlights over red chalk on tinted grounds, all so characteristic of Passeri's drawings, were all on occasion used by Maratti. Passeri's particular trademark is the red wash he so lavishly spread over the paper in the vast majority of his drawings. Another version of this composition, with St. Peter standing rather than seated, is at Düsseldorf (repr. Illa Budde, *Beschreibender Katalog der Handzeichnungen in der Staatlichen Kunstakademie Düsseldorf*, Düsseldorf, 1930, no. 392, pl. 60).

EXHIBITIONS: Scholz Exhibitions: Hamburg, 1963, no. 111, pl. 53; New Haven, 1964, no. 69.

Janos Scholz

Gian Antonio Burrini

Bologna 1656–Bologna 1727

139 *The Descent from the Cross*

Pen and brown ink, brown and red wash, over red chalk. 16$\frac{7}{16}$ × 11 inches (41.7 × 27.9 cm.). Lined.

Drawing fixed to a Mariette mount inscribed *ANTONIUS BURRINI.*

According to Mariette, who once owned this drawing, it formed part of a series of twelve studies for paintings on copper executed by Burrini for a certain Count P. C. A.; "Je crois Albergati, pour lequel Burrini a beaucoup travaillé," comments Mariette. "Ces dessins lui font assurément honneur. Ils sont pleins de feu. M. Chuberé les avoit apportés à Paris et j'en ai eu quatre à son inventaire, dont je fais cas." In addition to the present drawing, Mariette's group of four included a *Birth of the Virgin*, now in the Louvre (Inv. 7067), an *Adoration of the Shepherds*, and a *Presentation in the Temple*. Crozat owned an *Adoration of the Magi* from the original series of twelve, and an *Arrest of Christ* now in Dr. Einar Perman's collection in Stockholm may well have formed part of the set. Burrini, a minor but vigorous late seventeenth-century Bolognese master, drew the way he painted, in a loose, fluid, and pictorial fashion that owes much to the example of his teacher, Domenico Canuti.

PROVENANCE: Count Albergati, Bologna (?); M. Chuberé, Paris; Pierre-Jean Mariette (Lugt 1852); Mariette sale, Paris, 1775–1776, part of no. 238; purchased by the Metropolitan Museum in London, 1961.

BIBLIOGRAPHY: Mariette, *Abécédario*, I, p. 236.

The Metropolitan Museum of Art Rogers Fund, 61.123.4

Paolo Gerolamo Piola

Genoa 1666–Genoa 1724

140 *The Toilet of Bathsheba*

Pen and brown ink, brown and gray wash, heightened with white, over black chalk, on blue-green paper. 11$\frac{1}{2}$ × 17 inches (29.3 × 43.1 cm.).

Inscribed on verso in pen and brown ink, *Paolo Gerol.^{mo} Piola L . . .; No 29. L 10.*

Paolo Gerolamo Piola was the pupil of his father, Domenico, but at the end of the century, from 1690 to 1694, he worked under Carlo Maratti in Rome. The two influences are apparent in this drawing: the style and technique reflect the example of Domenico Piola, while the composition is directly derived from Maratti's *Toilet of Bathsheba*, painted about 1693 for Prince Adam Liechtenstein (repr. Voss, p. 345). The characteristic Genoese tendency to think in ornamental terms is recognizable in Paolo Gerolamo's transformation of Maratti's stately vertical composition into an oval suitable for insertion into the decorative scheme, as a stucco-framed wall panel or an overdoor.

EXHIBITIONS: Dayton, Genoese Masters, 1962–1963, no. 94, repr.; Hamburg, Scholz Exhibition, 1963, no. 116, pl. 65; New York, Finch College, Genoese Painters, 1964–1965, no. 84, repr.

Janos Scholz

Plates

I · JACOPO DA EMPOLI · Young Man Seen from the Back   The Pierpont Morgan Library

2 · CAMILLO PROCACCINI · Martyrdom of a Female Saint   The Metropolitan Museum of Art

3 · CRISTOFANO RONCALLI · Holy Family with Angels   The Metropolitan Museum of Art

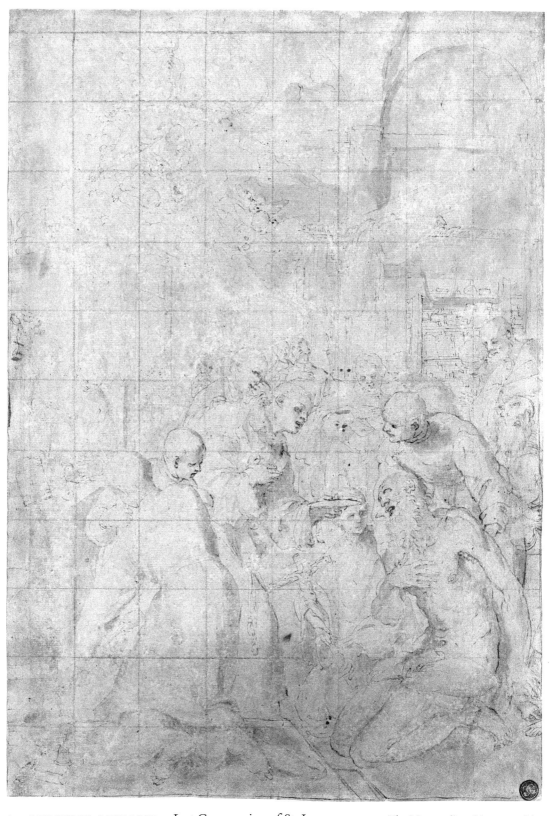

4 · LUDOVICO CARRACCI · Last Communion of St. Jerome   The Metropolitan Museum of Art

5 · AGOSTINO CARRACCI · Portrait of a Woman   Curtis O. Baer

6 · AGOSTINO CARRACCI · Woodland and Stream

Icaro e Dedalo

7 · AGOSTINO CARRACCI · Landscape with Icarus and Daedalus   Curtis O. Baer

8 · LUDOVICO CIGOLI · Study for a Figure of Christ

9 · ANNIBALE CARRACCI · The Monster Cacus

10 · ANNIBALE CARRACCI · Landscape with Jacob Sleeping
The Metropolitan Museum of Art

11 · ANNIBALE CARRACCI · Anteros Victorious
The Metropolitan Museum of Art

12 · ANNIBALE CARRACCI · Flying Putto   Janos Scholz

13 · ANNIBALE CARRACCI · Study of an Angel   The Metropolitan Museum of Art

14 · ANNIBALE CARRACCI · Shepherd with Pipes, and Two Dancing Children; Virgin and Child

Private Collection

15 · ANNIBALE CARRACCI OR STUDIO · Frontispiece, from the *Illustrations of the Life of St. Paul*
The Pierpont Morgan Library

15A · ANNIBALE CARRACCI OR STUDIO · Paul Preaching to Felix and Drusilla, from the *Illustrations of th*
Life of St. Paul

16 · BELISARIO CORENZIO · Joshua Stopping the Sun

17 · G. B. CARACCIOLO · David with the Head of Goliath

Janos Schol

Mrs. Richard Krautheimer

19 · GUIDO RENI · Solomon's Idolatry

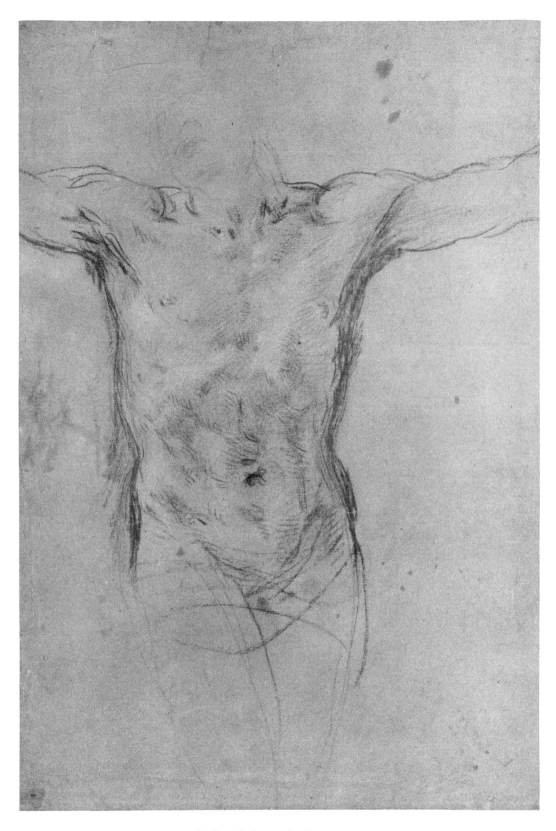

20 · GUIDO RENI · Torso: Study for Christ on the Cross   The Pierpont Morgan Library

2I · GUIDO RENI · Headless Body of Holofernes   The Metropolitan Museum of Art

22 · TANZIO DA VARALLO · Group of Soldiers with Pikes The Pierpont Morgan Library

23 · LEONELLO SPADA · David with the Head of Goliath
Robert and Bertina Suida Manning

24 · GIACOMO CAVEDONE · Half-Figure of a Woman with Arms Outstretched

25 · MATTEO ROSSELLI · Archer, and Three Studies of His Hands

Janos Scholz

26 · OTTAVIO LEONI · Portrait of a Boy: Pietro Altemps
The Pierpont Morgan Library

27 · OTTAVIO LEONI · Portrait of Settimia Manenti   The Pierpont Morgan Library

28 · DOMENICHINO · Landscape

Curtis O. Baer

29 · DOMENICHINO · Fortifications Seen across a River   The Pierpont Morgan Library

30 · BERNARDO STROZZI · Head of a Woman   Robert and Bertina Suida Manning

4 . . . .

31 · GIOVANNI LANFRANCO · St. Sylvester and the Dragon   The Pierpont Morgan Library

 48

32 · GIOVANNI LANFRANCO · Two Studies of a Head   Janos Scholz

33 · GIOVANNI LANFRANCO · Seated Apostles and Putti

34 · GIOVANNI LANFRANCO · Martyrdom of the Apostle Matthias   The Metropolitan Museum of Art

35 · G. B. DISCEPOLI · Joseph Sold by His Brethren

36 · GUERCINO · Virgin Giving the Scapular to St. Albert   The Pierpont Morgan Library

37 · GUERCINO · Youth Kneeling before a Prelate   The Metropolitan Museum of Art

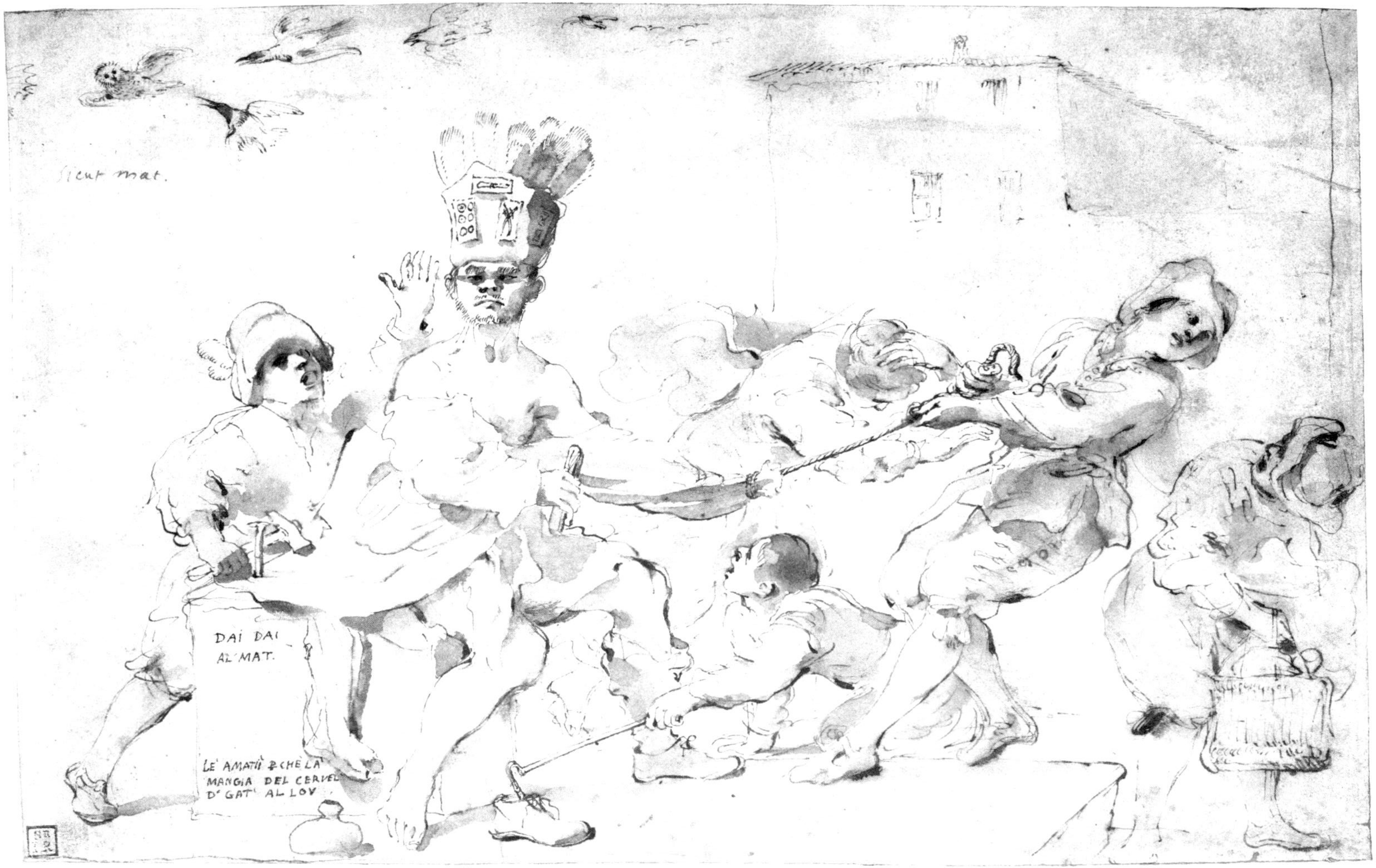
Sicut mat.
DAI DAI
AL MAT.
LE' AMATII P CHE LA
MANGIA DEL CERVEL
D' GAT' AL LOV

38 · GUERCINO · Satire on Gambling

The Pierpont Morgan Library

39 · GUERCINO · Visitation

38 · GUERCINO · Satire on Gambling

40 · GUERCINO · Martyrdom of St. John and St. Paul

40 (verso) · GUERCINO · Martyrdom of St. John and St. Paul

41 · GUERCINO · Martyrdom of St. Bartholomew The Pierpont Morgan Library

43 · GUERCINO · St. Philip Neri

J. Theodor Cremer

44 · GUERCINO · St. Philip Neri

45 · GUERCINO · Silvio Discovering the Wounded Dorinda   The Pierpont Morgan Library

47 · GUERCINO · Virgin and Child with a Book and a Pot of Pinks The Pierpont Morgan Library

48 · GUERCINO · Holy Family The Pierpont Morgan Library

49 · GUERCINO · Fireworks in a Piazza

Janos Scholz

50 · GUERCINO · Landscape with a Volcano

51 · GUERCINO · River Landscape with Swimmers

Janos Scholz

53 · PIETRO DA CORTONA · The Queen of Sheba Bringing Presents to Solomon

54 · PIETRO DA CORTONA · Offering to Pomona

55 · PIETRO DA CORTONA · St. Catherine of Alexandria

Janos Scholz

56 · PIETRO DA CORTONA · Nymphs Carving on Trees   The Pierpont Morgan Library

57 · PIETRO DA CORTONA · Triumph of Nature over Art   The Metropolitan Museum of Art

59 · PIETRO DA CORTONA · Woman Holding the Papal Tiara

60 · PIETRO DA CORTONA · Study of Two Figures for the *Age of Gold* Walter C. Baker

61 · PIETRO DA CORTONA · Study of a Seated Youth for the *Age of Gold*   Walter C. Baker

62 · PIETRO DA CORTONA · Study for the *Age of Bronze*   The Metropolitan Museum of Art

63 · PIETRO DA CORTONA · Study for the *Age of Bronze*   Walter C. Baker

64 · PIETRO DA CORTONA · Wind God

The Metropolitan Museum of Art

Benjamin Sonnenberg

66 (above and below) · PIETRO DA CORTONA · Angels Sealing the Foreheads of the Children of Israel
The Metropolitan Museum of Art

center section

right section

left section

67 · G. L. BERNINI · Portrait of a Youth (Self-Portrait?)   Mr. and Mrs. Lester F. Avnet

68 · G. L. BERNINI · Portrait of Cardinal Scipione Borghese   The Pierpont Morgan Library

69 · G. L. BERNINI · Portrait of Sisinio Poli
The Pierpont Morgan Library

70 · G. L. BERNINI · Study for the Tomb of Cardinal Domenico Pimentel
The Pierpont Morgan Library

71 · G. L. BERNINI · Caricature

Janos Schol:

72 · DANIELE CRESPI · St. Sebastian   The Pierpont Morgan Library

73 · ANDREA SACCHI · Allegory of Divine Wisdom   The Cooper Union Museum

74 · ANIELLO FALCONE · Martyrdom of a Male Saint   The Metropolitan Museum of Art

Ritratto di Masaniello.

75 · ANIELLO FALCONE · Portrait of Masaniello

76 · G. B. CASTIGLIONE · God the Father Appearing to Abraham and His Family

The Metropolitan Museum of Art

77 · G. B. CASTIGLIONE · Youth Playing a Pipe for a Satyr

78 · G. B. CASTIGLIONE · Five Nude Male Figures Punishing Another

79 · G. B. CASTIGLIONE · Five Despairing or Angry Figures

80 · G. F. GRIMALDI · Landscape with a Bridge and Two Figures

81 · CECCO BRAVO · A Dream

82 · CECCO BRAVO · Youthful St. John the Baptist   Janos Scholz

83 · PIETRO TESTA · Charity

The Pierpont Morgan Library

84 (verso) · PIETRO TESTA · Death of Sinorix

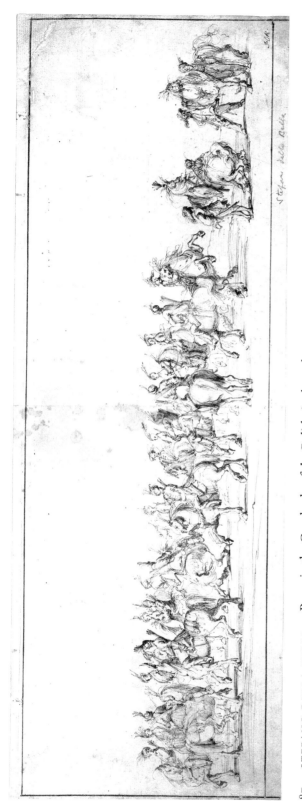

Stefano della Bella

87 · STEFANO DELLA BELLA · Pages in the Cavalcade of the Polish Ambassador

The Pierpont Morgan Library

88 · STEFANO DELLA BELLA · Stag Hunt

The Pierpont Morgan Library

89 · STEFANO DELLA BELLA · Two Women and Their Dogs Watching Deer

Private Collection

90 · STEFANO DELLA BELLA · Nude Man Pounding
Robert and Bertina Suida Manning

91 · STEFANO DELLA BELLA · Design for a Monstrance
The Metropolitan Museum of Art

92 · G. F. ROMANELLI · Construction and Restoration of Churches under Countess Matilda

The Pierpont Morgan Library

93 · G. F. ROMANELLI · Countess Matilda Giving Shelter to Bishop Anselm
The Pierpont Morgan Library

F. II. N.º 562.

Robert and Bertina Suida Manning

F. II. No 508.

95 · G. F. ROMANELLI · Prudence and Foresight

Robert and Bertina Suida Manning

96 · GIULIO CARPIONI · Studies of Bacchus and Ariadne
The Pierpont Morgan Library

97 · BALDASSARE FRANCESCHINI · Allegory in Honor of Vittoria della Rovere
Janos Scholz

Donald P. Gurney

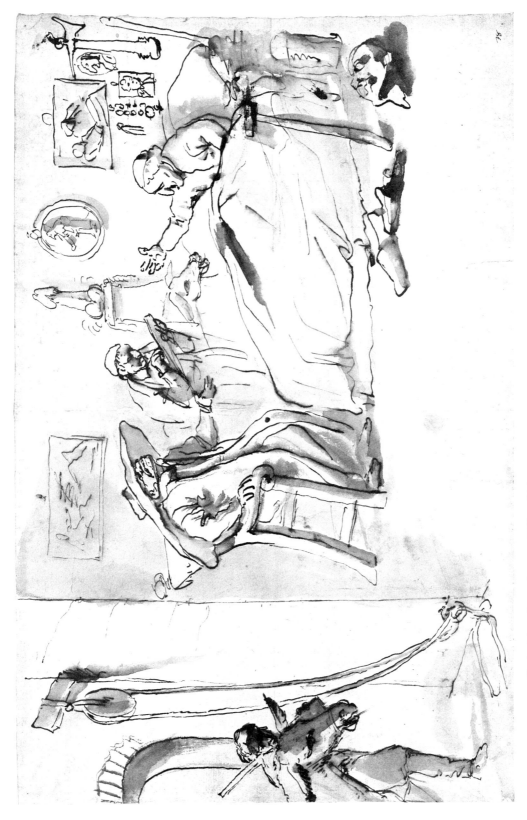

100 · P. F. MOLA · Cleric Dictating His Last Will and Testament

101 · P. F. MOLA · The Impoverished Artist   The Pierpont Morgan Library

102 · P. F. MOLA · Conversion of St. Paul

Janos Scholz

104 · MATTIA PRETI · Flying Figure Appearing before an Enthroned Figure

The Metropolitan Museum of Art

105 · SALVATOR ROSA · Witches' Sabbath   The Metropolitan Museum of Art

106 (opposite) · SALVATOR ROSA · The Prodigal Son Kneeling Among Swine
The Metropolitan Museum of Art

107 · SALVATOR ROSA · St. Philip Baptizing the Eunuch
The Pierpont Morgan Library

Bernardo
Cavallino

109 · BERNARDO CAVALLINO · The Virgin Immaculate   Janos Scholz

110 · D. M. CANUTI · Jupiter Astride His Eagle, with Psyche and a Putto

III · CARLO MARATTI · Allegorical Figure of Divine Wisdom
The Metropolitan Museum of Art

112 · CARLO MARATTI · Virtue Crowned by Honor
The Metropolitan Museum of Art

113 · CARLO MARATTI · Virtue Crowned by Honor
The Metropolitan Museum of Art

115 · CARLO MARATTI · Jael Slaying Sisera

116 · CARLO MARATTI · The Virgin Immaculate and Four Male Saints
The Pierpont Morgan Library

117 · CARLO MARATTI · The Virgin Immaculate and Four Male Saints
The Metropolitan Museum of Art

Francesco Castiglione Genovese.

118 · FRANCESCO CASTIGLIONE · Congress of Animals

119 · DOMENICO PIOLA · Rest on the Flight into Egypt

Robert and Bertina Suida Manning

120 · DOMENICO PIOLA · Time and a Woman Holding the Sun and the Moon

121 · BARTOLOMEO BISCAINO · Rest on the Flight into Egypt   The Pierpont Morgan Library

122 · CRESCENZIO ONOFRI · Landscape

123 · LUCA GIORDANO · Neptune Triumphant

Janos Scholz

124 · LUCA GIORDANO · Last Judgment Mrs. Richard Krautheimer

126 · CIRO FERRI · The Circumcision

Donald P. Gurney

127 · G. M. MITELLI · "In His Own House, Each Is King"   The Pierpont Morgan Library

128 · G. B. BEINASCHI · Two Studies of a Youth Playing a Trumpet

Janos Scholz

129 · ANDREA CELESTI · Allegory of Venetian Power The Metropolitan Museum of Art

130 · ELISABETTA SIRANI · Finding of Moses   The Metropolitan Museum of Art

131 · G. B. GAULLI · Joseph's Dream   Robert and Bertina Suida Manning

132 · G. B. GAULLI · Allegory of the Mathematical Sciences
Robert and Bertina Suida Manning

Greg° Deferrari

133 · GREGORIO DE' FERRARI · Infant Bacchus and Infant Satyr with a Lion
Robert and Bertina Suida Manning

134 · M. A. FRANCESCHINI · Chastity
The Metropolitan Museum of Art

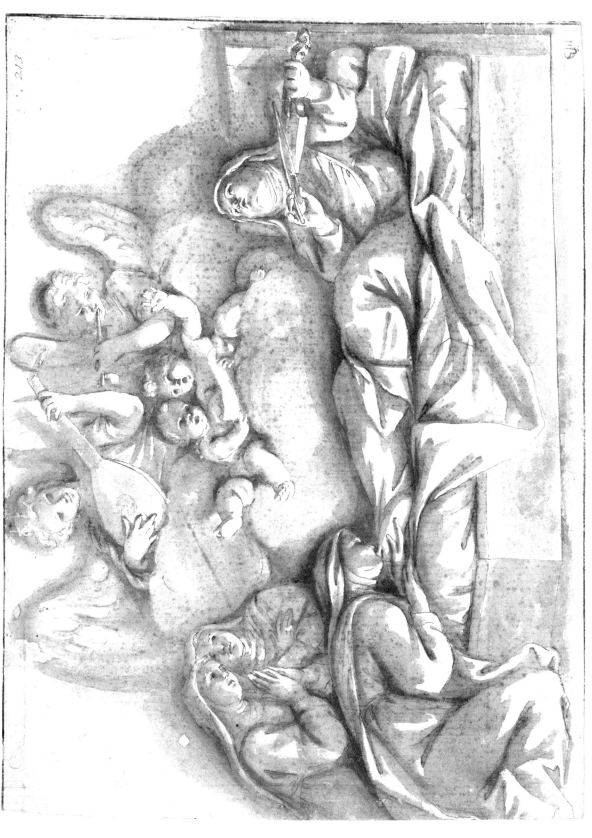

135 · M. A. FRANCESCHINI · Scene from the Life of S. Caterina dei Vigri

The Cooper Union Museum

136 · G. B. FOGGINI · Sabine Women Pleading for Peace

137 · A. D. GABBIANI · Two Hermit Saints in the Wilderness

138 · GIUSEPPE PASSERI · St. Peter in Prison

Janos Scholz

139 · G. A. BURRINI · Descent from the Cross The Metropolitan Museum of Art

Index of Artists

Designed by Peter Oldenburg. Text composed and printed in English Monotype Bembo by Clarke & Way, Inc., illustrations printed by The Meriden Gravure Company, on Stevens-Nelson Text. Binding by J. F. Tapley Co. First printing, 1967, 5500 copies.